W9-AMX-456

The Comic Tales of Chaucer

by the same author

THE TUDOR INTERLUDE

Leicester University Press

1958

T. W. CRAIK

The Comic Tales of Chaucer

UNIVERSITY PAPERBACKS

METHUEN : LONDON

First published 1964 by Methuen & Co
First published in University Paperbacks 1967, c1964

Printed in Great Britain
by T. & A. Constable Ltd, Printers
to the University of Edinburgh

Distributed in the USA
by Barnes & Noble Inc

University Paperbacks are published by
METHUEN & CO LTD
11 *New Fetter Lane London EC4*

To my brother

After tea we sate by the fire comfortably. I read aloud *The Miller's Tale.*

DOROTHY WORDSWORTH'S
Journal, 26 DECEMBER 1801

Contents

I am indebted to the Houghton Mifflin Company for permission to quote from F. N. Robinson's edition of THE POETICAL WORKS OF CHAUCER; *to Messrs Routledge and Kegan Paul Ltd for permission to quote from* SOURCES AND ANALOGUES OF CHAUCER'S CANTERBURY TALES *edited by W. F. Bryan and Germaine Dempster; to Professor B. Ford for permission to quote from an essay by David Holbrook in* THE AGE OF CHAUCER, *the first volume of the* GUIDE TO ENGLISH LITERATURE *of which he is the general editor; and to Professor R. M. Lumiansky for permission to quote from hi book* OF SONDRY FOLK.

Preface

This book is intended for the reader who already knows and enjoys Chaucer's poetry, but who is not necessarily a specialist in literature. My great object is to increase his enjoyment of Chaucer's comic tales, and thereby to increase his admiration of Chaucer. By giving an account of the tales one by one, and by comparing and contrasting them in the process, I have tried to point out some of their particular merits, and also to show some general features of Chaucer's art as well as his perpetual freshness and variety.

The full extent of Chaucer's variety can be appreciated only by reference to his whole work. It is not my purpose to exalt these comic tales above the rest of *The Canterbury Tales*, though all of them date from his latest period, when he was at the height of his powers, and though I think that it may be truly said of him (as Johnson said of Shakespeare) that 'in comedy he seems to repose, or to luxuriate, as in a mode of thinking congenial to his nature'.

Chaucer, as his readers are well aware, is not among those writers whose works can be easily, or profitably, classified into the tragic and comic categories: witness his greatest completed work, *Troilus and Criseyde*. Here he is undertaking to tell a tragic story in a tragic manner:

The double sorwe of Troilus to tellen,
  That was the kyng Priamus sone of Troye,
In lovynge, how his aventures fellen

Fro wo to wele, and after out of joie,
My purpos is, er that I parte fro ye.
  Thesiphone, thow help me for t'endite
  Thise woful vers, that wepen as I write.

Yet cheerfulness is always breaking in, and this is not to the damage of the poem but to its infinite enrichment. Again, *The Knight's Tale* has a happy ending:

And thus with alle blisse and melodye
Hath Palamon ywedded Emelye.
And God, that al this wyde world hath wroght,
Sende hym his love that hath it deere aboght;
For now is Palamon in alle wele,
Lyvynge in blisse, in richesse, and in heele,
And Emelye hym loveth so tendrely,
And he hire serveth al so gentilly,
That nevere was ther no word hem bitwene
Of jalousie or any oother teene.
Thus endeth Palamon and Emelye;
And God save al this faire compaignye!

Yet what we most strongly recall from the tale is the force of destiny, expressing itself in the tragedy of Arcite's death. And, yet again, the fabric of the whole poem is shot through with Chaucer's characteristic humour and good sense. The speech of Theseus, when he and his courtiers come upon Palamon and Arcite fighting their duel in the woods, has the same boisterous ringing gaiety as some of Pandare's exhortations to the lovesick Troilus:

Who may been a fool, but if he love?
Bihoold, for Goddes sake that sit above,

Se how they blede! be they noght wel arrayed?
Thus hath hir lord, the god of love, ypayed
Hir wages and hir fees for hir servyse!
And yet they wenen for to been ful wyse
That serven love, for aught that may bifalle.
But this is yet the beste game of alle,
That she for whom they han this jolitee
Kan hem therfore as muche thank as me.
She woot namoore of al this hoote fare,
By God, than woot a cokkow or an hare!

This jovial speech, coming from the mythical hero and the embodiment of knightly virtue, gives to the world of legend and idealism that substantial and human quality which we always find in Chaucer's best work, whether its final effect be gay or melancholy.

It would, then, be impossible to write on 'Chaucer's comedy' without mentioning almost everything he wrote. Even to pick out the 'comic tales' from *The Canterbury Tales* is perhaps somewhat arbitrary; for though there is general agreement that some tales are not comic at all, and others hardly at all, there may be disagreement about certain tales. My present principle has been to discuss those tales of which the direct and distinct purpose, as I see it, is to raise merriment. I have therefore not included *The Franklin's Tale*. It has a happy ending, and it gives great pleasure, but it provokes few smiles and no laughs. Nor have I included *The Manciple's Tale*, in spite of the line, ludicrous in itself and doubly ludicrous in its context,

This crowe sang 'Cokkow! cokkow! cokkow!'

Even *The Wife of Bath's Tale* has been excluded, after some hesitation, because humour is not the essence of the tale, though there is abundant humour in the comic despair of the knight who has been obliged to marry the loathly lady:

> Now wolden som men seye, paraventure,
> That for my necligence I do no cure
> To tellen yow the joye and al th'array
> That at the feeste was that ilke day.
> To which thyng shortly answeren I shal:
> I seye ther nas no joye ne feeste at al;
> Ther nas but hevynesse and muche sorwe.
> For prively he wedded hire on a morwe,
> And al day after hidde hym as an owle,
> So wo was hym, his wyf looked so foule.
> Greet was the wo the knyght hadde in his thoght,
> Whan he was with his wyf abedde ybroght;
> He walweth and he turneth to and fro.
> His olde wyf lay smylynge everemo,
> And seyde, 'O deere housbonde, *benedicitee*!
> Fareth every knyght thus with his wyf as ye?
> Is this the lawe of kyng Arthures hous?
> Is every knyght of his so dangerous?'

There is an element of grim humour in the irony of *The Pardoner's Tale* ('No lenger thanne after Deeth they soughte'), and the tale produces a feeling of moral satisfaction, but nobody would call it comic. By contrast, *The Friar's Tale*, though like the Pardoner's it is a story carrying a moral warning, is obviously designed to bring summoners into contempt and derision, and the comic spirit pervades it, as I shall try to show.

Mention of the Pardoner will remind readers that Chaucer often gives a comic context to tales which are not themselves comic. Indeed, mirth is the prevailing mood of the prologues and epilogues which link the stories together, and the comic tales often derive added comic power from the way in which they are introduced. I shall accordingly discuss the prologues and epilogues of the comic tales in the chapters which follow, but the human comedy of the whole pilgrimage is outside my present scope. It is universally agreed that in creating the pilgrims and in imagining their intercourse, Chaucer showed his genius: the tales often bear upon each other, and upon their tellers, in such a way as to tend towards making a single great poem out of a series of great poems, and they cannot be torn from their dramatic context without loss. I am far from suggesting that they should be read apart from their context; but I think it is a worse mistake (which has marred much critical work on Chaucer) to concentrate so thoroughly upon that context that one does not, properly speaking, read the tales at all, but uses them as hunting-grounds in which to trace the tracks (real or supposed) of their tellers.[1] It is chiefly as a poet-storyteller that I wish to consider him.

Like Shakespeare, Chaucer usually took over the stories of others; and, again like Shakespeare, he made them his own. His borrowed story is simply his starting-point – as we can see whenever a source or analogue survives. But it *is* his starting-point, however far he may depart from it; it always remains at the core of each tale, particularly of those comic tales like the Miller's which depend so much upon a neat dovetailing of events. Now when an author begins with a ready-made story, there

[1] For example: 'It seems likely that the Miller-Reeve acquaintanceship must be of long standing, that the Miller worked years ago as servant boy in the Reeve's household at the time when the Reeve, then a carpenter, was made a cuckold by a cleric.' (R. M. Lumiansky, *Of Sondry Folk*, Austin, Texas 1955, p. 51.)

are necessarily limits to what he can do with it, and if he cannot work within those limits he must abandon that story and get another. Milton's difficulties with the story of *Paradise Lost* are notorious, and so are Shakespeare's with the story of *Measure for Measure*. In the event, Milton and Shakespeare persuade us to overlook their unsolved difficulties, because they succeed in their most important aims. Nevertheless, some stories are better than others, and a great narrative artist like Chaucer shows his greatness in choosing his material as well as in handling it.

The virtue of a good story, needless to say, is not simply that it gives its writer no trouble. It can be, and frequently is, a source of inspiration to him, suggesting how he can make it even better. Again and again, working upon bare events and the outlines of character, Chaucer makes the characters produce the events, turns coincidence into necessity, and breathes spontaneous life into his creation. His central interest lies in human nature, and his insight into human nature is that of a poet. We may say, then, that the story itself, *as* story, has a personality of its own, and that Chaucer chooses it because it appeals to his own personality, as man and as poet, and treats it in such a way as to bring out its essential quality. I am convinced that this weighed more with him than any desire to express through a tale the personality of a pilgrim, even though the dramatic use of the pilgrims was his invention, and though he aptly couples tales and tellers whenever he can. The dramatic framework is not what gives the tales their excellence; it is an added attraction to tales excellent in themselves.

In my quotations from Chaucer I have used the text of F. N. Robinson's original edition (Cambridge, U.S.A.,

1933), but I have altered his punctuation in order to conform to British usage, and also on a very few occasions to improve (as I think) the sense. I gratefully acknowledge the permission to quote from this and other works protected by copyright. Beyond this, acknowledgment becomes a difficult matter, and precise acknowledgment a virtual impossibility. A great deal has been written on *The Canterbury Tales*, and no one who adds to these writings can say exactly how much his ideas owe to the ideas of others, especially if he has been enjoying Chaucer for a long time before contemplating writing a book on him. My brother, to whom I dedicate this book, introduced me to *The Canterbury Tales* when I was twelve years old, and it is to him, and to my pupils at Cambridge and Leicester during the last dozen years, that I feel myself most indebted. I have, of course, read Chaucer's major critics with interest, and often with admiration, though the critic who has most influenced my whole approach to Chaucer's many-sided art is not a Chaucerian but a Shakespearian, Harley Granville Barker. My excuse for this book, in which I must repeat many things which others have said already, is that there seems still something new and true to say.

I *The Miller's Tale*

The Miller's Tale is the first comic tale in *The Canterbury Tales*, and the second tale to be told. It follows *The Knight's Tale* of Palamon and Arcite, a romantic story of two noble kinsmen engaged in fatal rivalry for the love of Emelye. Chaucer's object is, of course, the variety which comes from contrast, a 'cherles tale' after a 'noble storie'; but he makes the contrast more amusing by showing why the Miller insists on interrupting the Host's orderly scheme, whereby the Monk shall tell

'Somwhat to quite with the Knyghtes tale.'

The Miller, who is drunk, announces

'I kan a noble tale for the nones,
With which I wol now quite the Knyghtes tale.'

The comedy results not merely from rebellious drunkenness but also from misunderstanding: the Miller really does believe that his own tale is a worthy counterpart to the Knight's, being likewise a rousing story about rival lovers. The contrast and the parody are the funnier because the Miller is unaware of them. He is simply telling the best story he knows, a story so good and so *apropos* that he cannot bear to defer it till a later time, even though he knows he is too drunk to be perhaps the master of his tongue. He has no other motive, certainly not to anger the Reeve, whose outburst takes him completely by surprise, and to whom he replies in tones of sweet reasonableness, unaware of the concealed reason for the Reeve's objection:

> 'Why artow angry with my tale now?
> I have a wyf, pardee, as well as thow.'

Chaucer has told us, in the *General Prologue*, that the Reeve has been formerly a carpenter, so that we understand his absurd touchiness which so puzzles the Miller; and when the Reeve tells his own tale, his malice is clearly announced at the beginning and repeated at the end. Thus Chaucer achieves variety again, this time in the motivation of the story-teller, though as a story the Reeve's tale is very like the Miller's. If the Miller meant to ridicule the Reeve, this contrast would be lost. But the Miller is all innocence, in his treatment of the Reeve and of the Host alike, disarmingly blaming his drunken slips of speech on the latter's good ale. Once he has gained his end, the permission to tell his tale, his drunken obstreporousness melts away, to be replaced by universal good humour.

This is important, because Chaucer himself wants to use a similar tone in order to placate the possibly indignant reader. Like the Miller, Chaucer is all innocence, but Chaucer's innocence is an ironical, assumed innocence. Just as the Miller blames the ale for his drunkenness, so Chaucer blames the Miller for *The Miller's Tale*. He pretends to be bound by the historian's responsibilities, and further pretends that he finds them irksome: he is sorry to have to repeat a churl's tale in a churl's terms, but he must,

> Or elles falsen som of my mateere.

But we know perfectly well that Chaucer is telling the

tale for his own pleasure, and that the Miller himself is no more than Chaucer's own creation. Thus we are amused, but not surprised, when the tone of earnest supplication –

> And therfore every gentil wight I preye,
> For Goddes love, demeth nat that I seye
> Of yvel entente –

is soon modified into the cavalier, take-it-or-leave-it tone of

> And therfore, whoso list it nat yheere,
> Turne over the leef, and chese another tale;

and thence changes into downright puckish mischief:

> Blameth nat me if that ye chese amys.
> The Millere is a cherl, ye knowe wel this;
> So was the Reve, and othere manye mo,
> And harlotrie they tolden bothe two.

Chaucer is thus amusingly establishing his right to tell comic tales, for their own sake, whenever and however he pleases. He makes use of the Miller for various reasons: to forestall any objection to indecorous tales; to underline the contrast between a 'noble storie' and a 'cherles tale' which treats the rivalry of lovers in a spirit of farce; and to introduce one of the comic and dramatic dialogues between his pilgrims, dialogues which help to connect the tales with each other, as well as delightfully creating the personalities of their tellers.

Once *The Miller's Tale* is begun, however, Chaucer has no further use for the Miller or the other pilgrims, until he needs them again for the Reeve's prologue; and then, a single line is enough to do his business:

> This tale is doon, and God save al the rowte!

What might be called the personal touches in the tale are such as any narrator would use, and indeed are such as Chaucer does use in those poems where he is himself the only story-teller:

> . . . I may nat rekene hem alle.

> Now, sire, and eft, sire, so bifel the cas,
> That on a day . . .

> And thus they been accorded and ysworn
> To wayte a tyme, as I have told biforn.

> A myrie child he was, so God me save.

> I dar wel seyn, if she hadde been a mous,
> And he a cat, he wolde hire hente anon.

> This passeth forth; what wol ye bet than weel?

Certainly these touches are frequent, and the frequency may be due to Chaucer's conscious use of a narrator; but they are no different in kind from remarks like

> For ay the ner the fir, the hotter is, –
> This, trowe I, knoweth al this compaignye.[1]

It is hardly necessary to point out that the commentary is sometimes sophisticated beyond the abilities of the Miller; on the carpenter's marriage, for example:

> He knew nat Catoun, for his wit was rude,
> That bad man sholde wedde his simylitude.

Chaucer no more desires to impoverish the tale by suppressing his own sophistication than he desires to muddle

[1] *Troilus and Criseyde,* I, 449-450. The best, and shortest, discussion of the relationship between tales and tellers is Kenneth Sisam's, in his Introduction to *The Nun's Priest's Tale* (Oxford, 1927), pp. xl-xlii.

it by imitating the Miller's drunken incoherence. What he does is, in a word, to tell the Miller's tale for him, using all his own poetic resources. As for Chaucer's attitude to the story, it in no way differs from the Miller's, since the Miller intends no offence in the world, and the story is told for its own comic sake.

It may in a sense be said that the story tells itself. If we assume, as is possible, that its two elements, that of the predicted flood and that of the misdirected kiss, were already combined in the story as it reached Chaucer, then the sequence of events must be in the following order: after mention has been made of the husband, his wife, and her two lovers, the first lover conspires with the wife to deceive her husband with a pretended prophecy of a flood; the conspiracy is successful and the husband takes refuge in a tub hanging in the roof, while the lover lies with the wife; the second lover inopportunely arrives, bargains with the wife for a kiss, is mocked by her, and revenges himself on the first lover who is unwisely trying to repeat the insult, thus producing the comic confusion which brings the farce to an end.

The tale is essentially a farce, with a farce's predominance of comic situation over everything else. Of course, one immediately objects that in Chaucer's hands it is not left as a mere farce: the characters, the settings, the situations are all more substantial and more plausible than the bare necessities of farce require. Yet *The Miller's Tale*, perhaps in this respect the most elaborate of Chaucer's comic stories, has something in common with one of his baldest, *The Shipman's Tale*: neither of them is told in ridicule of any particular one of the characters, as *The Reeve's Tale* is told of Symkyn, as *The*

Merchant's Tale is told of Januarie, or as a summoner and a friar are demolished in *The Friar's Tale* and *The Summoner's Tale*. This is not to say that in these two tales there is no ridicule, any more than that in the other four there is nothing but satire, or that the satire is limited to its principal butt (May and Damyan instantly spring to mind). But it is very clear that *The Miller's Tale* carries no moral lesson, still less any satire on a professional class. The carpenter is ridiculed, not as a carpenter, but as a doting and jealous husband and as a credulous and superstitious man. His being a carpenter is needed only for his convenient absences at Osney or at the abbot's grange (absences which any other craft would have explained equally well), and for his practical preparation of a way of escape from the flood ('His owene hand he made laddres thre'). Even his personal failings are not dwelt on – as are those of Symkyn or Januarie – but are used, like Nicholas's presumptuous vanity and Absolon's affected fastidiousness, to motivate the plot and to sway our sympathies as the plot requires; for all three men have to undergo some rough treatment in the story, and the story is improved if this rough treatment results in part from their own behaviour. The wife, Alison, always an agent and never a victim, is treated with so much enthusiasm that nobody could imagine poetic justice to be Chaucer's concern in this tale, even though some may be meted out, in passing, to Absolon and Nicholas and John.

In *The Miller's Tale*, whatever may be his purpose in the later comic tales of the series, Chaucer is concerned primarily with the telling of a farcical story. But, being Chaucer, he is not content to tell it in a crude and elementary way, though its general course may have been firmly marked out for him in advance. His whole poetic genius goes into the telling.

We see his peculiar art as early as the first half-dozen lines:

> Whilom ther was dwellynge at Oxenford
> A riche gnof, that gestes heeld to bord,
> And of his craft he was a carpenter.
> With hym ther was dwellynge a poure scoler,
> Hadde lerned art, but al his fantasye
> Was turned for to lerne astrologye . . .

Most story-tellers, one imagines, would begin with the old carpenter and his young wife, a traditional foundation on which to build a comic intrigue. By disposing of the carpenter, for the present at least, in a couplet and a half, Chaucer suggests that the story's chief interest will lie elsewhere, and that the scholar is worth more of our time. We are meant to recall the short account of the tale given by the Miller in his prologue –

> For I wol telle a legende and a lyf
> Both of a carpenter and of his wyf,
> How that a clerk hath set the wrightes cappe –

and to recognize in this 'poure scoler' the hero of this intrigue. This is a further use to which Chaucer has put the Miller, as a result of whose hint we expect the clerk to use his astrology and weather-prediction as a means of deceiving the carpenter. This expectation is confirmed by what we are now told:

> This clerk was cleped hende Nicholas.
> Of deerne love he koude and of solas;
> And therto he was sleigh and ful privee,
> And lyk a mayden meke for to see.

Nicholas is a charming and gallant dissembler. Chaucer describes him by means of his possessions and his accomplishments. He has a private room in the house, necessary to his later intrigue, but here suggesting refinement and exclusiveness; and in this room, which is scented, like his own person, he keeps his astrological books and instruments, and a psaltery, to the accompaniment of which he sings in the evenings. He is, as has been often noted, the antithesis of the idealized studious Clerk of Oxford in the *General Prologue*, and there radiates from him an air of frivolous yet attractive gaiety, like that of the summer grasshopper in the fable:

> Ful often blessed was his myrie throte.
> And thus this sweete clerk his tyme spente
> After his freendes fyndyng and his rente.

When Chaucer now introduces the carpenter's newly-married young wife, it is immediately clear that Nicholas is to be her fate. Her husband does not foresee it; but he nevertheless mingles jealousy with his dotage:

> This carpenter hadde wedded newe a wyf,
> Which that he lovede moore than his lyf;
> Of eighteteene yeer she was of age.
> Jalous he was, and heeld hire narwe in cage,
> For she was wylde and yong, and he was old,
> And demed hymself been lik a cokewold.

And her description – one of Chaucer's best – presents her as beautiful, lively, and impossible to tame or even to cage:

> Fair was this yonge wyf, and therwithal
> As any wezele hir body gent and smal.

Details of her person and clothing are set down as randomly as if Chaucer were drawing from a figure in constant motion. His first glance falls upon the girdle about her waist and the apron over her hips, carrying on the 'weasel' image of sinuous activity. From accumulating the details of her dress, where the contrast of white silk and black embroidery is striking, he suddenly turns his eyes to her face and dramatically meets her own:

> And sikerly she hadde a likerous ye;
> Ful smale ypulled were hire browes two,
> And tho were bent and blake as any sloo.

Next comes a cluster of images expressing her beauty, youth, animation and sexual attractiveness; her costume itself tempts Chaucer's wandering eye towards her charms, and leads his mind to ponder her aptitudes:

> A brooch she baar upon hir lowe coler,
> As brood as is the boos of a bokeler.
> Hir shoes were laced on hir legges hye.
> She was a prymerole, a piggesnye,
> For any lord to leggen in his bedde,
> Or yet for any good yeman to wedde.

She is evidently ill matched with the old churl her husband, and a fit morsel for Nicholas, whom we may suppose to have noted all that Chaucer has noted, and to be merely waiting for the first chance of recommending himself. That chance now immediately comes – Chaucer wastes no time on their growing acquaintance –

> Whil that hir housbonde was at Oseneye:

the casual reference to his usual place of work adds to our feeling of familiarity with the characters' daily life.

The clerk and the young wife soon come to an understanding. Indeed, it is plain that they understand each other from the first. Nicholas, though he is 'lyk a mayden meke for to see', is a vigorous, even a violent, wooer:

> And prively he caughte hire by the queynte,
> And seyde, 'Ywis, but if ich have my wille,
> For deerne love of thee, lemman, I spille.'
> And heeld hire harde by the haunche-bones,
> And seyde, 'Lemman, love me al atones,
> Or I wol dyen, also God me save!'
> And she sproong as a colt dooth in the trave,
> And with hir heed she wryed faste away,
> And seyde, 'I wol nat kisse thee, by my fey!
> Why, lat be', quod she, 'lat be, Nicholas,
> Or I wol crie "out, harrow" and "allas"!
> Do wey youre handes, for youre curteisye!'

The wife's mingled simplicity and sophistication is just what Chaucer's account of her has foretold: 'And she sproong as a colt dooth in the trave' shows us the instinctive struggles of a wild unbroken animal ('Wynsynge she was, as is a joly colt'), but her unfulfilled threats to cry out for help suggest coquetry. Her reluctance having been, in due form, displayed and overcome, she accepts Nicholas as her lover, warning him to give her jealous husband no further grounds for jealousy. She says that she fears for her life, and though of course this is her melodramatic way of making their situation a romantic one, the carpenter needs to be made a man to be reckoned with, lest he should become an object of our pity. Nicholas scorns the danger, reducing the situation to its true petty proportions:

> 'A clerk hadde litherly biset his whyle,
> But if he koude a carpenter bigyle.'

His boast, as well as being a first taste of that vanity which will be wanted at the climax of the story, foreshadows the ingenious plan which he will use against the carpenter, and stresses the gulf which lies between the man of art and the man of craft. The scene ends with Nicholas in his glory:

> Whan Nicholas had doon thus everideel,
> And thakked hire aboute the lendes weel,
> He kiste hire sweete and taketh his sawtrie,
> And pleyeth faste, and maketh melodie.

Chaucer's direct passage to the next incident is masterly:

> Thanne fil it thus, that to the paryssh chirche,
> Christes owene werkes for to wirche,
> This goode wyf went on an haliday.
> Hir forheed shoon as bright as any day,
> So was it wasshen whan she leet hir werk.
> Now was ther of that chirche a parissh clerk,
> The which that was ycleped Absolon.

The wife's pious errand is amusing in itself, coming straight after Nicholas's courtship (though not, of course, on the same day), and after her solemn oath 'that she wol been at his comandement' at the first opportunity. There is also a hint that she goes to church chiefly to be admired, and this hint immediately precedes Absolon's entry into the story. We therefore jump to the conclusion that he too is to be an admirer of hers, and further conclude that after Nicholas's success he comes too late.

He might have some prospects of supplanting Nicholas, despite his late arrival, if he were not so obviously a comic figure. The name Absolon (surely never given to an English child at baptism!) creates the effect of caricature from the start, and leads straight to a grotesque image:

> Crul was his heer, and as the gold it shoon,
> And strouted as a fanne large and brode.

Just as Nicholas is the antithesis of the Clerk of Oxford, so 'joly Absolon' is the ape of the Squire, exaggeratedly 'a lovyere and a lusty bacheler', diligently fantastic in person and in dress, but undisguisably commonplace:

> His rode was reed, his eyen greye as goos.
> With Poules wyndow corven on his shoos,
> In hoses rede he wente fetisly.

The Squire was singing or fluting all the day; Nicholas is for ever within reach of his psaltery; and Absolon likewise must have an abundance of the necessary accomplishments, and show them off all over the town:

> In twenty maner koude he trippe and daunce
> After the scole of Oxenforde tho,
> And with his legges casten to and fro,
> And pleyen songes on a smal rubible;
> Therto he song som tyme a loud quynyble;
> And as wel koude he pleye on a giterne.
> In al the toun nas brewhous ne taverne
> That he ne visited with his solas,
> Ther any gaylard tappestere was.
> But sooth to seyn, he was somdeel squaymous
> Of fartyng, and of speche daungerous.

The last couplet, abruptly finishing his description, comes as a surprise. His delicacy seems out of character after his good-fellowship among the lively barmaids, and looks more like the affectation of refinement than refinement itself. As for the word 'fartyng', for which nothing has prepared us, it is here punched home so that we will recall it much later at the point of Abolson's discomfiture, which it now helps to foreshadow.

Meanwhile, Chaucer returns to the present, 'the haliday' on which the carpenter's wife has visited the parish church. Absolon is officiating with his censer, ogling the women with his usual indiscrimination until his eye dwells on the newcomer to the parish:

> And many a lovely look on hem he caste,
> And namely on this carpenteris wyf.
> To looke on hire hym thoughte a myrie lyf,
> She was so propre and sweete and likerous.
> I dar wel seyn, if she hadde been a mous,
> And he a cat, he wolde hire hente anon.

And in his mind he forms a plan which he executes when the night comes, as Chaucer makes it do straightway:

> The moone, whan it was nyght, ful brighte shoon,
> And Absolon his gyterne hath ytake,
> For paramours he thoghte for to wake.

He sings a love-song beside the carpenter's bedroom window. It is a 'shot-wyndowe', for it will be required to open on its hinges later in the story, but Chaucer draws no particular attention to it here; it is enough that we see Absolon playing the fool outside it. Both he and it will now be ready for future use. But in preparing for later developments, Chaucer improves the present moment also. The carpenter – as is only natural – hears Absolon:

This carpenter awook, and herde him synge,
And spak unto his wyf, and seyde anon,
'What, Alison! herestow nat Absolon,
That chaunteth thus under oure boures wal?'
And she answerde hir housbonde therwithal,
'Yis, God woot, John, I heere it every deel.'
This passeth forth; what wol ye bet than weel?

Alison emphatically implies her conscious innocence of having given Absolon any encouragement; and her husband, his jealous doubts allayed, goes on ignoring the real cause for suspicion, which comes not from the parish clerk but from Nicholas. Chaucer thus neatly sums up the quadrilateral situation by means of a comic little scene of dramatic irony, and then launches into a fanciful account of Absolon's energetic, elaborate, continuous, tiresome, and wholly unsuccessful pursuit of Alison, who of course cares only for Nicholas. That he should woo her 'fro day to day' with a stream of messages and presents, under her husband's nose, is hardly realistic, yet it is necessary if his obsession with her is to be vividly presented. Besides, allusion to such things as oven-hot wafers and miracle-plays helps to make the whole life of the town, and hence that of the characters, substantial and convincing; it serves the same purpose as the carpenter's work at Osney, the taverns frequented by Absolon, the assembly of the women at the parish church, and some otherwise unnecessary details of Absolon's portrait ('Wel koude he laten blood and clippe and shave,/And maken a chartre of lond or acquitaunce)'. To mingle realistic detail with absurd impossibilities, so that the impossibilities become equally believable, is one of Chaucer's most successful devices in his farcical tales.

His habit of gradually, imperceptibly, releasing information likewise helps to give substance to settings and to characters. In the bedroom dialogue between the carpenter and his wife, we learn their names without recognizing that we are hearing them for the first time (not many readers remember that Nicholas does not use Alison's in their earlier scene together). In just the same way the names of the pilgrims themselves are often withheld until a suitable occasion ('Abyd, Robyn, my leeve brother'; 'leve brother Osewold').

Not only personal names, but personal dispositions, are kept in reserve. The personages thus appear to act spontaneously and not in mere spasmodic obedience to the dictates of the story. The character of John the carpenter – of whom we have hitherto been told only that he is old, rich, a churl, and suspicious – is developed in the next episode. The development is interesting in itself, for everyone likes to improve his acquaintance with Chaucer's characters, and it is also closely relevant both to the plot and to the subtle comedy of human relationships which Chaucer gratuitously adds to the comedy of situation.

And so bifel it on a Saterday,
This carpenter was goon til Osenay.

Remembering what happened last time he went to Osney, we are ready for the information, briefly given, that Nicholas and Alison agree on a plan whereby 'she sholde slepen in his arm al nyght'. Clearly the story has begun moving towards its climax; and 'al nyght' not only looks forward to the certain cuckolding of the carpenter but to the possible reappearance of Absolon at the window, since his recent appearance there is fresh in our memory. Incidentally, Chaucer glosses over the fact that the lovers could go to bed at any time when the carpenter was away from home: a few moments in a pear-tree are as much as *The Merchant's Tale* permits to Damyan and May. But *The Miller's Tale* depends on a night of confusion, and therefore Nicholas and Alison are content with nothing less than a whole night of love. As for Absolon's reappearance, a necessity of the story, Chaucer throws out nothing so strong as a hint; he never anticipates his surprises, but he foreshadows them in such a way that they remain surprises while seeming (when they come) the necessary results of character and situation. Nor does he let us into the lovers' plot. We are told just enough of it to be able to measure its successful effect, stage by stage, upon the carpenter. Nicholas retires to his private room, amply provisioned, and stays there in mysterious concealment.

This is on a Saturday. On the Sunday, at sunset, the carpenter duly notices his lodger's absence. The old man's character is wonderfully suggested. As he gets older, he observes how suddenly death seems to come to his acquaintances:

> God shilde that he deyde sodeynly!
> This world is now ful tikel, sikerly.
> I saugh to-day a cors yborn to chirche
> That now, on Monday last, I saugh hym wirche.

The idea growing upon him, he is consumed with curiosity, and straightway sends his servant upstairs to investigate. There follows a scene of action, the like of which we have not had since Nicholas violently declared his love to Alison. The servant's energy ('He cride and knokked as that he were wood'), and his enterprise in peeping through the cat-hole, are dramatically contrasted with the stillness of Nicholas:

> This Nicholas sat evere capyng upright,
> As he had kiked on the newe moone.

Chaucer has wisely avoided recent mention of Nicholas's astrology, lest we should guess the lovers' plan; but this reference to the new moon jogs our memory, as well as introducing the carpenter's appropriate ruminations, which further reveal his own character:

> This carpenter to blessen hym bigan,
> And seyde, 'Helpe us, seinte Frydeswyde!
> A man woot litel what hym shal bityde.
> This man is falle, with his astromye,
> In som woodnesse or in som agonye.
> I thoghte ay wel how that it sholde be!
> Men sholde nat knowe of Goddes pryvetee.
> Ye, blessed be alwey a lewed man,
> That noght but oonly his bileve kan!
> So ferde another clerk with astromye;
> He walked in the feeldes, for to prye
> Upon the sterres, what ther sholde bifalle,
> Til he was in a marle-pit yfalle;
> He saugh nat that. But yet, by seint Thomas,
> Me reweth soore of hende Nicholas.
> He shal be rated of his studiyng,
> If that I may, by Jhesus, hevene kyng!
> Get me a staf, that I may underspore,
> Whil that thou, Robyn, hevest up the dore.
> He shal out of his studiyng, as I gesse' –
> And to the chambre dore he gan hym dresse.

The old man's sympathetic concern for his deceiver both enriches his own character and underlines the dramatic irony of the situation, but Chaucer takes care that we do not feel sorry for him: his speech is full of unmistakable complacency, which further improves the irony. Just as Nicholas boasted that a clerk could easily deceive a carpenter, the carpenter now boasts that he always foresaw the lodger's breakdown, makes a virtue out of his own ignorance, derides clerks for their curiosity, and promises himself the satisfaction of saying all this to Nicholas. The poetry perfectly captures his mood, with the exultation of 'Ye, blessed be alwey a lewed man', the scornful reiteration of 'studiyng' and of 'astromye' (he neither knows nor cares that he has mistaken the latter word), and the nod of stern relish in the pause after the abrupt 'He saugh nat that'. We do not, accordingly, pity him as an innocent victim of clerkly guile. Nor do we pity him as an elderly victim of youth, for he is still strong and active; when he and his servant have forced the door off its hinges, he takes Nicholas 'myghtily' by the shoulders and shakes him 'harde' to try to restore his senses.

He now displays the superstition of the ignorant, with his elaborate exorcism of evil spirits, a 'nyght-spel' which will not, however, protect him from being cuckolded the following night; and Nicholas, pretending to recover, reveals his pretended vision. Chaucer has skilfully shown the carpenter's superstitious simplicity before requiring to make use of it, so that now, when we learn Nicholas's plan for the first time, it seems well fitted to John's weaknesses, whereas in fact the weaknesses have been fitted to the plan. Nicholas plays also on John's curiosity, whetting it with his cryptic sigh –

'Allas!
Shal al the world be lost eftsoones now?' –

with his delays ('Fecche me drynke'), and his conspiratorial air ('I wol telle it noon oother man, certeyn'); and as an extra safeguard, he swears him to secrecy on pain of madness (a threat which we recall at the end of the tale). Only then does Nicholas utter his message, employing climax and inversion most dramatically:

> 'Now John', quod Nicholas, 'I wol nat lye;
> I have yfounde in myn astrologye,
> As I have looked in the moone bright,
> That now a Monday next, at quarter nyght,
> Shal falle a reyn, and that so wilde and wood,
> That half so greet was nevere Noees flood.
> This world', he seyde, 'in lasse than an hour
> Shal al be dreynt, so hidous is the shour.
> Thus shal mankynde drenche, and lese hir lyf.'
> This carpenter answerde, 'Allas, my wyf!
> And shal she drenche? allas, myn Alisoun!'
> For sorwe of this he fil almoost adoun,
> And seyde, 'Is ther no remedie in this cas?'
> 'Why, yis, for Gode', quod hende Nicholas . . .

The carpenter's mind turns instantly to his wife (the rhyme gives emphasis to his cry) of whom he is constantly thinking; but Chaucer's main object here is not to engage our unexpected sympathy for John's strong human feelings, or even to develop the irony of his concern for his traitress, but rather to keep us in mind of Nicholas's intentions towards Alison, so that we enjoy the animated urgency of his advice ('Hastow nat herd . . .?'; 'Hastou nat herd . . .?'; 'And therfore, woostou what is best to doone?'), and the advice itself. For his advice, whereby for the first time we have a glimpse of his plans, is hilarious. A day's food will be ample provision in the tubs, he insists, for the rain will begin at quarter-night (9 p.m.) and the flood-water will vanish next morning at prime (9 a.m.) – as soon, that is, as he shall have satisfied his desire. Thus twelve hours will accomplish what Noah's flood took some twelve months to do. Besides, after the Flood, God promised never again to destroy mankind. But the carpenter is no student of biblical history: having heard the tale of Noah 'ful yoore ago', he assumes that the apocryphal story of Noah's wife is authentic and that it therefore justifies Nicholas's requirement of three separate tubs. Apart from the comedy of character here, with the clerk gulling the carpenter, there is a theological joke, for we are told in *The Parson's Tale* (839) that 'by the synne of lecherie God dreynte al the world at the diluge', and here is Nicholas inventing a second deluge as a means to lechery. The joke, and the consequent irony, is carried on by his later recommendation

'Thy wyf and thou moote hange fer atwynne;
For that bitwixe yow shal be no synne,
Namoore in lookyng than ther shal in deede,
This ordinance is seyd. Go, God thee speede!'

On this point *The Parson's Tale* says (844) 'And nat oonly that God forbad avowtrie in dede, but eek he comanded that thou sholdest nat coveite thy neighebores wyf'. The husband is forbidden to sin with his own wife so that her lover may enjoy her. Meanwhile any suspicion he may feel is skilfully diverted from his lodger to his servants:

'But Robyn may nat wite of this, thy knave,
Ne eek thy mayde Gille I may nat save;

Axe nat why, for though thou aske me,
I wol nat tellen Goddes pryvetee.'

And an appeal to his vanity completes the conquest:

'Men seyn thus, "sende the wys and sey no thyng";
Thou art so wys, it needeth thee nat teche.
Go, save oure lyfe, and that I the biseche.'

Nicholas, having fooled him, praises his wisdom; and Alison, preparing to betray him, implores him by her marriage bond:

'I am thy trewe, verray wedded wyf;
Go, deere spouse, and help to save oure lyf.'

John the carpenter is left filled with apprehension and heroic responsibility:

Lo, which a greet thyng is affeccioun!
Men may dyen of ymaginacioun,
So depe may impressioun be take.
This sely carpenter bigynneth quake;
Hym thynketh verraily that he may see
Noees flood come walwynge as the see
To drenchen Alisoun, his hony deere.
He wepeth, weyleth, maketh sory cheere;
He siketh with ful many a sory swogh;
He gooth and geteth hym a knedyng trogh . . .

Chaucer makes us share the carpenter's vivid imaginings, and then, by repetition of rhythm, passes with comical swiftness from his passionate mood to his practical actions. John victuals the three tubs and secretly hangs them in the roof, and he makes three ladders. As always in the tale, detail is used to give substance to the material objects: 'a knedyng trogh', 'a tubbe and a kymelyn', 'breed and chese, and good ale in a jubbe'; the ladders have their 'ronges' and 'stalkes'. Nothing is forgotten; the servants are sent to London on business. At last, 'on the Monday, whan it drow to nyght', the three retire to their tubs, where they sit in darkness and silence, the carpenter waiting for the rain, and the lovers waiting for their opportunity, which soon arrives:

> The dede slepe, for wery bisynesse,
> Fil on this carpenter right as I gesse
> Aboute corfew-tyme, or litel moore;
> For travaille of his goost he groneth soore,
> And eft he routeth, for his heed myslay.
> Doun of the laddre stalketh Nicholay,
> And Alisoun ful softe adoun she spedde;
> Withouten wordes mo they goon to bedde,
> Ther as the carpenter is wont to lye.
> Ther was the revel and the melodye;
> And thus lith Alison and Nicholas,
> In bisynesse of myrthe and of solas,
> Til that the belle of laudes gan to rynge,
> And freres in the chauncel gonne synge.

The organization here is, as usual, superb. The carpenter's sleep, related to the 'wery bisynesse' of his preparations, is not only opportune but plausible. It is also realistic and comic, Chaucer's balanced lines bringing together his spiritual and bodily discomfort; while the groans and snores, furthermore, provide the signal for Nicholas and Alison to slink off to the comfort of the bed where the now uncomfortable husband usually sleeps. He is stupefied with 'wery bisynesse'; they are active in 'bisynesse of myrthe and of solas'. The line 'Ther was the revel and the melodye' is vigorously suggestive, recalling Nicholas's courtship scene, and it harmonizes with the following images of ringing bells and singing friars, though the piety of celibates also provides a piquant contrast to the scene within the carpenter's house. It is, incidentally, some time since we were outside the house (over 250 lines), and the church-image from the town prepares us for something new from that quarter; in particular from 'This parissh clerk, this amorous Absolon'.

Once again Chaucer most expertly draws together the elements of his plot. His original account of Absolon renders his casual trip to Osney, 'with compaignye, hym to disporte and pleye', very likely; and the chain of evidence which convinces Absolon that John is away at the abbot's grange is equally plausible. John, as we know, has taken care not to be seen about his secret business with the tubs and ladders; and so his apparent absence from home and his certain absence from Osney seem conclusive, and encourage Absolon to go as a wooer to the window of the room where we have just left Alison in bed with Nicholas. The soliloquy in which he comes to this resolution develops his character, as he foresees his success; at the same time it foreshadows events by making us anticipate his discomfiture:

> 'So moot I thryve, I shal, at cokkes crowe,
> Ful pryvely knokken at his wyndowe
> That stant ful lowe upon his boures wal.
> To Alison now wol I tellen al
> My love-longynge, for yet I shal nat mysse
> That at the leeste wey I shal hire kysse.
> Som maner confort shal I have, parfay.
> My mouth hath icched al this longe day;
> That is a signe of kissyng atte leeste . . .'

This assurance of a kiss is kept before us as Absolon prepares for his visit; he dresses gaily, combs his hair (a neat reminder of all his would-be-romantic foppishness), and takes care of his breath by chewing cardamom and liquorice. And now once again he is standing by the shot-window:

> 'What do ye, hony-comb, sweete Alisoun,
> My faire bryd, my sweete cynamome?
> Awaketh, lemman myn, and speketh to me!'

If he only *knew* what she was doing, he would not so inappositely bid her awake. He woos her with odd scraps of the Song of Solomon, incongruous in this scandalous circumstance, and yet comically apt in the mouth of the parish clerk; and he improves his text with vulgar unromantic conceits of his own ('for youre love I swete ther I go'). The pathetic appeal meets a downright refusal:

> 'Ywis, lemman, I have swich love-longynge,
> That lik a turtel trewe is my moornynge.
> I may nat ete na moore than a mayde.'
> 'Go fro the wyndow, Jakke fool', she seyde;
> 'As help me God, it wol nat be "com pa me".
> I love another – and elles I were to blame –
> Wel bet than thee, by Jhesu, Absolon.
> Go forth thy wey, or I wol caste a ston,
> And lat me slepe, a twenty devel wey!'

Alison's angry reply, besides fitly ridiculing Absolon's affected courtship (which she treats as if it were the caterwauling of tom-cats), underlines the irony of the present situation: her firm oath that she loves another is true of Nicholas, though of course she intends Absolon to understand it of her husband; and her expressed desire to sleep undisturbed, designed to confirm Absolon's mistaken idea that she is alone in the house, reminds us that in fact she and her lover have been disturbed in their 'bisynesse of myrthe and of solas'. Thus, though her ready wit recalls her similar handling of Absolon's previous visit, the humour is here partly at her expense.

The dramatic situation is now speedily resolved. Absolon agrees to go away in return for a kiss (though he hopes 'ther cometh moore' afterwards), and both he and Alison make themselves ready, Chaucer shifting his attention rapidly from the one to the other until he brings them together for the kiss. Though we know from her words to Nicholas ('Now hust, and thou shalt laughen al thy fille') that she means to mock Absolon, and from Absolon's deliberate preparations ('This Absolon doun sette hym on his knees'; 'This Absolon gan wype his mouth ful drie') that he will be mocked, we are almost as thoroughly taken by surprise as he is:

Derk was the nyght as pich, or as the cole,
And at the wyndow out she putte hir hole,
And Absolon, hym fil no bet ne wers,
But with his mouth he kiste hir naked ers
Ful savourly, er he were war of this.
Abak he stirte, and thoughte it was amys,
For wel he wiste a womman hath no berd.
He felte a thyng al rough and long yherd,
And seyde, 'Fy! allas! what have I do?'
'Tehee!' quod she, and clapte the wyndow to,
And Absolon gooth forth a sory pas.

Absolon's discomfiting experience is given in all the emphasis of detail ('with his mouth': how else?), and his farcical dismay is dramatized by the verse ('Abak he stirte'); his momentary bewilderment turns to outraged certainty in the instant before Alison claps the window to, and to revengeful determination as he hears her laughter and the voice of Nicholas within. In a frenzy of mortification and disgust he erases the mistaken kiss from his mouth, reversing now his earlier preparations –

Who rubbeth now, who froteth now his lippes
With dust, with sond, with straw, with clooth, with
chippes,
But Absolon –

at the same time erasing all his romantic follies for the future:

For he was heeled of his maladie.[1]

Chaucer thus prepares us, by making Absolon a sadder and a wiser man, to sympathize with his revenge and to take his part against Nicholas. The calmness with which he endures the smith's good-natured banter about 'som gay gerl', which touches Absolon nearer than Gerveys is aware, further suits this purpose.

Absolon borrows the hot ploughshare, leaving us not quite so mystified as the smith, whom he promises to enlighten 'to-morwe day' (it is still pitch-dark, a necessary condition of what follows), and returns across the

[1] A lover's 'siknesse and his sorwe' is conventionally cured by his lady's mercifulness (May bids Damyan 'been al hool', *The Merchant's Tale*, 2005-2010; Criseyde tells Troilus 'Now beth al hool, no lenger ye ne pleyne', *Troilus and Criseyde*, III, 168); but here Alison heals Absolon by her cruelty.

street to the carpenter's house. Here he affects to resume his character as a servile romantic lover, and offers Alison a gold ring in exchange for a kiss. The offer, and its sentimental expression ('My mooder yaf it me, so God me save'), are just plausible enough to deceive Nicholas as the story requires him to be deceived. But Chaucer improves the comedy by showing that Nicholas is the victim not only of Absolon's trick but of his own vanity, of which we have already had ample evidence:

> This Nicholas was risen for to pisse,
> And thoughte he wolde amenden al the jape;
> He sholde kisse his ers er that he scape.
> And up the wyndowe dide he hastily,
> And out his ers he putteth pryvely
> Over the buttok, to the haunche-bon;
> And therwith spak this clerk, this Absolon,
> 'Spek, sweete bryd, I noot nat where thou art.'
> This Nicholas anon leet fle a fart,
> As greet as it had been a thonder-dent,
> That with the strook he was almoost yblent;
> And he was redy with his iren hoot,
> And Nicholas amydde the ers he smoot.

Nicholas thinks to improve on the jest by himself insulting Absolon (the stress in 'He sholde kisse *his* ers er that he scape' suggests his glee, and so does his hasty throwing open of the window), and in his eagerness he overdoes the whole thing ('Over the buttok, to the haunche-bon'). Yet the abundant comedy is not wholly at Nicholas's expense when he presents such a sitting target. Absolon must discover whether the insult is to be repeated, so when he hears the window open, he says 'Spek, sweete bryd'; if silence follows, he will sweep to his revenge. But silence does not follow, and the coarse extempore repartee of Nicholas involves both revenger and victim in confusion. This, at least, we had not foreseen. Nor had we foreseen the sequel:

> Of gooth the skyn an hande-brede aboute,
> The hote kultour brende so his toute,
> And for the smert he wende for to dye.
> As he were wood, for wo he gan to crye,
> 'Help! water! water! help, for Goddes herte!'
> This carpenter out of his slomber sterte,
> And herde oon crien 'water' as he were wood,
> And thoughte 'Allas, now comth Nowelis flood!'
> He sit hym up withouten wordes mo,
> And with his ax he smoot the corde atwo,
> And doun gooth all;

The carpenter and the flood, both forgotten amid the rapidly-unfolding story, are brought back in the middle of a couplet; and John's literal downfall is immediately completed, for he is a man of action and loses no time in meditation.

The tale now briefly concludes, with the curious neighbours thronging in and the carpenter unable to get a serious hearing; for, just as Nicholas had warned him, he is reputed mad. This gives a neat ending to a story which obviously cannot go on; we may not enquire into the further married life of John and Alison (unlike that of Januarie and May in *The Merchant's Tale*), so we are diverted from it by the final chorus of laughter ('And turned al his harm unto a jape'; 'And every wight gan laughen at this stryf'), in which the comic summary invites us to join, with the pilgrims ('Whan folk hadde laughen at this nyce cas'):

Thus swyved was this carpenteris wyf,
For al his kepyng and his jalousye;
And Absolon hath kist hir nether ye;
And Nicholas is scalded in the towte.
This tale is doon, and God save al the rowte!

II *The Reeve's Tale*

The Miller's Tale ends with a peal of laughter from the deluded carpenter's neighbours, and the laughter is taken up by Chaucer's pilgrims:

> Whan folke hadde laughen at this nyce cas
> Of Absolon and hende Nicholas,
> Diverse folk diversely they seyde,
> But for the moore part they loughe and pleyde.
> Ne at this tale I saugh no man hym greve,
> But it were oonly Osewold the Reve.
> By cause he was of carpenteris craft,
> A litel ire is in his herte ylaft;
> He gan to grucche, and blamed it a lyte.

Only the Reeve is displeased, for the inadequate but understandable reason that he is himself a carpenter and therefore takes the discomfiture of John as a professional and even personal affront. Chaucer has evidently made him 'colerik' and a carpenter in order to motivate his anger (the couplet about his trade may have been put into the *General Prologue* as an afterthought while the prologues and tales of the Miller and the Reeve were being written); and the anger, dramatically interesting in itself, is used to launch another tale of robust coarse farce as well as to connect it with the tale just told. Chaucer, the reluctant historian, has earlier blamed the Miller for telling so gross a tale; the Reeve is now blaming the Miller for obliging him to tell another.

Neither excuse, of course, will hold water, though the Reeve thinks his does. There is good comedy of character here, as also in the Reeve's change of front: at first he decides to stand on his dignity as an old man, and not descend to the Miller's level:

> 'So theek', quod he, 'ful wel koude I yow quite
> With bleryng of a proud milleres ye,
> If that me liste speke of ribaudye.
> But ik am oold, me list nat pley for age . . .'

but in his digression on old age he forgets this original purpose, and 'I koude' becomes 'I shal':

> '. . . I shal hym quite anoon;
> Right in his cherles termes wol I speke.'

Resolving to beat the Miller at his own game, he embarks on his tale with the gusto it requires, while his resentment is equally suitable to the subject of the story, in which a miller's misdeeds meet with poetic justice.

This prologue, like that of *The Miller's Tale*, shows Chaucer's art in fitting the tales into apt dramatic contexts, or rather in creating dramatic contexts suitable to the traditional tales. As we have seen, the Miller's tale follows the Knight's as a kind of unintentional parody or antimasque, and for this reason precedes the Reeve's. But even if we set aside this reason, the tales of the Miller and the Reeve could not by their very nature be told in reversed order. The story of a jealous carpenter's gullibility would have been a poor rejoinder to the story of a miller's pride and greed. Symkyn's faults are heavier in themselves than John's; and moreover, whereas John's work is not related to his faults but merely to the plot, Symkyn's work is necessarily related to both. The story, in whatever form it reached Chaucer, turns upon a miller's theft, even though he may have specially adapted it to the Reeve's purpose in denouncing Symkyn as a type of all thieving millers.[1] He could not have adapted *The Miller's Tale* to serve an attack on carpenters, for it is a much richer story than the Reeve's, with the carpenter taking no part in the important incident of the misdirected kiss, and with the interest equally distributed between John, Alison, Nicholas and Absolon. Though he has brought the other characters in *The Reeve's Tale* to life (as he never fails to do), Chaucer has placed Symkyn the miller firmly in the centre of the stage, the others being always shown in reference to him: the clerks are his intended victims, and his actual vanquishers; his wife's pride reflects his own; his daughter has his 'camus nose'.

Accordingly, whereas *The Miller's Tale* opens with the barest mention of the carpenter, *The Reeve's Tale* opens with a full account of Symkyn's appearance and character. The portrait of the miller of Trumpington, like those of Nicholas, Alison and Absolon in *The Miller's Tale*, strikingly resembles the portraits of the pilgrims in the *General Prologue*. It is an accumulation of details, some of them unimportant and serving merely to give substance to the character and his setting (the mill is, of course, a water-mill) –

> Pipen he koude and fisshe, and nettes beete,
> And turne coppes, and wel wrastle and sheete –

[1] In the two French *fabliaux* (printed in *Sources and Analogues of Chaucer's 'Canterbury Tales'*, ed. W. F. Bryan and Germaine Dempster, Chicago, 1941; London 1958, pp. 126-147) the miller's theft of the corn is likewise essential, though the clerks' ingenuity is more elaborate than in Chaucer's rendering; at the end the miller is beaten by the clerks in revenge for his theft.

but most of them pointing to his chief qualities, which are pride, fierceness, strength and fraudulence. A comic effect is made by the listing of the weapons which he bore about him:

> Ay by his belt he baar a long panade,
> And of a swerd ful trenchant was the blade.
> A joly poppere baar he in his pouche;
> Ther was no man, for peril, dorste hym touche.

That sounds like the end of that subject – and then comes the postscript:

> A Sheffeld thwitel baar he in his hose.

His physique is brutal:

> Round was his face, and camus was his nose;
> As piled as an ape was his skulle;

and so is his disposition:

> He was a market-betere atte fulle.
> Ther dorste no wight hand upon hym legge,
> That he ne swoor he sholde anon abegge.

Yet with his brutality he combines low cunning:

> A theef he was for sothe of corn and mele,
> And that a sly, and usaunt for to stele.

The last line of his description, according to the manner of the *General Prologue*, announces his name; but like 'hende Nicholas' and 'joly Absolon' he is given an epithet, 'deynous Symkyn', to suggest his rôle in the coming story.

'Deynous' equally well describes Symkyn's wife,

whose portrait follows. Unlike the carpenter in *The Miller's Tale*, he has 'wedde his simylitude':

A wyf he hadde, ycomen of noble kyn;
The persoun of the toun hir fader was.
With hire he yaf ful many a panne of bras,
For that Symkyn sholde in his blood allye.
She was yfostered in a nonnerye;
For Symkyn wolde no wyf, as he sayde,
But she were wel ynorissed and a mayde,
To saven his estaat of yomanrye.
And she was proud, and peert as is a pye.

Though a celibate's natural daughter, she takes pride in being the natural daughter of Somebody, and in having had a socially respectable education. As for Symkyn, he has acquired all this prestige by marriage, while the parson's generous dowry shows the young yeoman as a socially impressive suitor who could make his own terms. And now, married for twenty years and more, they are a notable couple:

A ful fair sighte was it upon hem two;
On halydayes biforn hire wolde he go
With his typet bounden aboute his heed,
And she cam after in a gyte of reed,
And Symkyn hadde hosen of the same.
Ther dorste no wight clepen hire but 'dame';
Was noon so hardy that wente by the weye
That with hire dorste rage or ones pleye,
But if he wolde be slayn of Symkyn
With panade, or with knyf, or boidekyn.

The wife pert as a pie, Symkyn going before her like the

peacock he is ('As any pecok he was proud and gay'), these two are clearly strutting to some future downfall.

The firm emphasis on their pride suggests their social ambitions for their daughter, now of marriageable age; the suggestion is repeated in the ten satirical lines which follow the daughter's portrait, and which tell how her grandfather the parson intends her to make an even better alliance than the one which he arranged for her mother. But the portrait itself belies the social pretensions: blood will out, and the girl is Symkyn's own daughter:

> A doghter hadde they bitwixe hem two
> Of twenty yeer, withouten any mo,
> Savynge a child that was of half yeer age;
> In cradel it lay and was a propre page.
> This wenche thikke and wel ygrowen was,
> With kamus nose, and eyen greye as glas,
> With buttokes brode, and brestes rounde and hye;
> But right fair was hire heer, I wol nat lye.

She is sexually attractive, but in a solid, rustic way, very unlike the animated Alison of *The Miller's Tale*. Though two years older than Alison, she has none of her sophistication; she is just a grown-up child, and Chaucer gives her little more attention than he gives the baby.

> In cradel it lay and was a propre page.

'In cradel it lay'; and the cradle, as a shifting landmark, is to be more important than the baby it contains. In fact, both the cradled child and the marriageable daughter are introduced here in readiness to play their later part in their father's discomfiture.

With this discomfiture, and the roguery which it

punishes, all the rest of the short tale is concerned. Once the clerks Aleyn and John appear at the mill, all the characters are on stage together, and the action continues to the end in unity of time and place.

The clerks' appearance in the story is the direct result of the miller's bold fraudulence, for he has taken advantage of their manciple's sickness to steal 'outrageously', and has out-faced the protesting warden, who is perhaps therefore moved to give Aleyn and John permission to guard the next consignment of corn to the mill. The clerks need be little more than ministers of rough justice upon the miller, but Chaucer gives them particularity by making them Northerners and fellow-townsmen. This serves the additional purpose of marking them firmly off from the miller and his family, the only other speaking characters in the tale. He gives them also vivacity, and a self-confidence which we hear in their reported speech to the warden:

> Testif they were, and lusty for to pleye,
> And oonly for hire myrthe and revelrye
> Upon the wardeyn bisily they crye
> To yeve hem leve but a litel stounde,
> To goon to mille and seen hir corn ygrounde;
> And hardily they dorste leye hir nekke
> The millere sholde not stele hem half a pekke
> Of corn by sleighte, ne by force hem reve.

After what we have been told of Symkyn, it seems likely enough that he will use force, and we feel that Aleyn and John are only prudent in equipping themselves 'with good swerd and with bokeler by hir syde'. Instead it proves that Symkyn in his arrogance plays the clerks at their own game of cunning, and so these swords and bucklers are never used. However, they serve to notify us – and Symkyn – of the hostile undertone beneath the clerks' hearty explanation of their visit.

Some acquaintance exists between the clerks and the miller. This saves time, and also allows Aleyn to make a prophetic enquiry after the daughter whom he is later to seduce: 'Hou fares thy faire doghter and thy wyf?' The miller's reply –

> 'Aleyn, welcome', quod Symkyn, 'by my lyf!
> And John also, how now, what do ye heer?' –

shows that he sees well enough why they have come themselves instead of letting a servant take charge of the corn; and John's rejoinder, in spite of its assumed ease ('Hym boes serve hymself that has na swayn'), carries a challenge under the simple statement

> 'And forthy is I come, and eek Alayn,
> To grynde oure corn *and carie it ham agayn.*
> I pray yow spede us heythen that ye may.'

Symkyn, who does indeed mean to send them packing, pleasantly invites them to take themselves off:

> 'It shal be doon', quod Symkyn, 'by my fay!
> What wol ye doon whil that it is in hande?'

But John's retort, given force by oath and rhyme, is a downright refusal of this pressing invitation:

> 'By God, right by the hopur wil I stande',
> Quod John, 'and se how that the corne gas in.
> Yet saugh I nevere, by my fader kyn,
> How that the hopur wagges til and fra.'

His ignorance is only a feint, for he knows the name of

the hopper and how it works; and Symkyn is not taken in, for when Aleyn has justified his supervision of the meal as it falls into the trough,

> This millere smyled of hir nycetee,
> And thoghte, 'Al this nys doon but for a wyle.
> They wene that no man may hem bigyle,
> But by my thrift, yet shal I blere hir ye,
> For al the sleighte in hir philosophye . . .'

Like the carpenter in *The Miller's Tale*, he exalts himself over book-learned clerks, but on account of his cunning, not his simplicity. He turns their own precautions against them. While their eyes are riveted to the hopper and the trough, he steals out unperceived, looses their horse, and returns to work:

> This millere gooth agayn, no word he seyde,
> But dooth his note, and with the clerkes pleyde,
> Til that hir corn was faire and weel ygrounde.

Chaucer here suggests ('pleyde') the high tension and the rich irony of the situation: the clerks are elated by their triumphant guarding of the corn; while the miller hugs his private triumph, confident of stealing the meal while they recapture the horse. With a dramatic shift from the past tense to the present, John makes the discovery:

> And whan the mele is sakked and ybounde,
> This John goth out and fynt his hors away.

For twenty lines confusion reigns, and all is exclamation and activity. The horse's uncontrolled haste to the fen (and the wild mares), vividly described already, is pictured afresh in the speech of Symkyn's wife (who herself 'cam lepynge inward with a ren'), and the clerks vanish after it into the distance at top speed. By contrast, the scene closes on the miller's calm, deliberate theft of a half-bushel of the meal. We may notice that Chaucer, having used the wife to direct the clerks after their horse, has her conveniently at hand to receive her husband's instructions about making the stolen meal into a cake (so that it shall not be found on the premises), and thereby makes her a party to the theft; she acts also as audience for Symkyn's self-satisfied speech as he watches the distant pursuit of the horse ('Lo, wher they goon! ye, lat the children pleye'), while the speech itself serves to carry us back to the clerks.

Chaucer takes little time in relating how they recapture their horse, though it takes them till nightfall to do it. He is more concerned with the consequences. John and Aleyn cannot now get back to Cambridge; for though John needed no guide to the mill, to journey through the fenland in darkness is a different matter. Therefore, 'wery and weet, as beest is in the reyn', they trudge back to the mill, knowing well that the miller will have stolen their meal, and foreboding the sarcasm which the warden and their companions will pour on their misplaced self-confidence. At the mill their enemy awaits them, comfortable in body and mind:

> The millere sittynge by the fyr he fond.

Symkyn expresses his good-humour in satirical jesting about the lodging he can offer them, and about their clerkly ingenuity:

> 'Myn hous is streit, but ye han lerned art;
> Ye konne by argumentes make a place
> A myle brood of twenty foot of space.'

John and Aleyn have to laugh at his jest:

> 'Ay is thou myrie, and this is faire answerd';

they have to flatter him, and they have to show their money (though, as later appears, this is not handed over, the reckoning standing till their departure). Like their earlier dialogue with him, this exchange is given tension by their unexpressed feelings. Symkyn, on the contrary, is relaxed and convivial. He sends his daughter (who has taken no previous part in the tale) to buy ale and bread; he roasts a goose of his own for supper, makes a great parade of securing the horse which he turned free ('it sholde namoore go loos'), and prepares the clerks' bed a few yards from his own in the single room shared by the whole family, cradle and all. We take for granted these sleeping arrangements, essential to the future events, because of the miller's spontaneous jest about them; and the events themselves are made more plausible by the hearty drinking that accompanies supper, for the miller drinks himself nearly insensible, and his wife drinks herself into high spirits.

All go to bed 'aboute mydnyght', and the miller and his family are soon asleep ('hem nedede no dwale'). Their snores, and his own mortification, keep Aleyn awake, and he curses them all, man, wife and daughter:

> 'Wha herkned evere slyk a ferly thyng?
> Ye, they sal have the flour of il endyng.
> This lange nyght ther tydes me na reste';

but then he sees how he can use his enforced wakefulness to redeem his ruined self-respect:

> 'But yet, nafors, al sal be for the beste.
> For John,' seyde he, 'als evere moot I thryve,
> If that I may, yon wenche wil I swyve.'

He wants 'esement' for his wrongs since he cannot have 'amendment' of them. It becomes clear at this point that Symkyn's trickery, which has forced the clerks to lodge overnight in his house, will recoil upon his own family, and we enjoy the poetic justice of this, even while we smile at the clerkly sophistry of Aleyn's argument that by satisfying his natural lusts he is merely claiming his legal rights. Our sympathies are, of course, entirely with Aleyn, especially when he fearlessly ignores John's warning that the miller is a physical match for the two of them:

> Aleyn answerde, 'I counte hym nat a flye.'
> And up he rist, and by the wenche he crepte;
> This wenche lay uprighte, and faste slepte,
> Til he so ny was, er she myghte espie,
> That it had been to late for to crie,
> And shortly for to seyn, they were aton.
> Now pley, Aleyn, for I wol speke of John.

This last line surprises us when we read the tale for the first time. Aleyn's seduction of the daughter looks like the climax, yet here is Chaucer leaving him and turning to the prudent John, who has remained uninterestingly in his own bed; but the complications of the story are only just beginning.

John envies his friend's successful venture, and gloomily foresees his own inglorious rôle in the story which Aleyn will boastfully tell to all their other friends. To prevent this fate, he determines to be adventurous in his turn, and quietly removes the cradle to the foot of his own bed. This is less logical but more dramatic than the account in the French *fabliau* versions, where he moves the cradle because he has seen the miller's wife get up and go out of the room. Chaucer's version, besides making a better transition from Aleyn to John, keeps up expectation (why is John moving the cradle?), and gives a sudden delight when the wife does get up (thus making John's moving of the cradle seem nothing less than inspiration). Her rising is made into yet another effect of the drinking at supper ('wente hire out to pisse'), and her return produces fine dramatic irony:

> 'Allas!' quod she, 'I hadde almoost mysgoon;
> I hadde almoost goon to the clerkes bed.
> Ey, benedicite! thanne hadde I foule ysped.'[1]

Yet her entering the wrong bed is not, in one respect, her misfortune:

> Withinne a while this John the clerk up leep,
> And on this goode wyf he leith on soore.
> So myrie a fit ne hadde she nat ful yoore;
> He priketh harde and depe as he were mad.

John is both eagerly restoring his self-esteem and making up for lost time.

> This joly lyf han thise two clerkes lad
> Til that the thridde cok bigan to synge.

[1] In the French versions, the wife is getting back into her own bed when the clerk draws her attention to the cradle's position by pulling the baby's ear; Chaucer wisely lets sleeping babies lie, and instead makes the wife feel for the cradle. The French versions are loaded with ingenious but superficial contrivance of this sort. For example, the miller locks his daughter in a bin for the night, and pushes in the key after her through a hole; later she gives the key to the clerk through the same hole so that he can unlock the bin (which evidently opens only from outside) and get in. He then wins her by the gift of a ring, supposedly of gold and having the magic power to restore lost virginity, but really made of base metal and taken off the andiron.

Chaucer, with his usual brisk neatness, takes no more than these two lines to sum up the clerks' successes, to bring the dawn, and thereby to switch our attention from the enthusiastic energies of John to the failing energies of Aleyn:

> Aleyn wax wery in the dawenynge,
> For he had swonken al the longe nyght,
> And seyde, 'Fare weel, Malyne, sweete wight!
> The day is come, I may no lenger byde;
> But everemo, wher so I go or ryde,
> I is thyn awen clerk, swa have I seel!'

Subtle as ever, Aleyn conceals his satiety under a romantically conventional prudence, and takes a sentimental farewell, as if he were Troilus parting from Criseyde at the unwelcome break of day.[1] His courtly behaviour so impresses the stupid girl that she tells him where to find the cake made from the stolen meal. Thus the wheel beautifully comes full circle: figuratively speaking, Aleyn eats his cake and has it; he gets 'esement' and 'amendment' too.

No sooner have we relished this position than the climax of farcical complication is upon us. Aleyn goes straight from his triumph back into danger, by repeating (in reverse) the wife's mistake. He finds the cradle:

> 'By God', thoughte he, 'al wrang I have mysgon.
> Myn heed is toty of my swynk to-nyght,
> That makes me that I ga nat aright.
> I woot wel by the cradel I have mysgo;
> Heere lith the millere and his wyf also.'

[1] *Troilus and Criseyde*, III, 1415-1526.

This is even funnier than the dramatic irony of the wife's mistake ('I hadde almoost goon to the clerkes bed'), for, after all, he is half right, and the miller's wife *is* there.

> And forth he goth, a twenty devel way,
> Unto the bed ther as the millere lay.

Chaucer, having come to the climax of the tale, is not afraid to drive home the dramatic irony of the farce by emphatic repetition and inversion:

> He wende have cropen by his felawe John,
> And by the millere in he creep anon,
> And caught hym by the nekke, and softe he spak.

His boastfulness, at which John's soliloquy has already hinted ('whan this jape is tald another day'), will not allow him to wait till they are clear of the miller's house, or even till John awakes. He must wake John up this moment, and pour his triumph into his ears, while taking care ('softe he spak') that the sleeping miller in the next bed does not hear him. Therefore, with elaborate caution, he awakens the supposed John:

> He seyde, 'Thou John, thou swynes-heed, awak,
> For Cristes saule, and heer a noble game.
> For by that lord that called is seint Jame,
> As I have thries in this shorte nyght
> Swyved the milleres doghter bolt upright,
> Whil thow hast, as a coward, been agast.'
> 'Ye, false harlot', quod the millere, 'hast?
> A! false traitour! false clerk!' quod he,
> 'Thow shalt be deed, by Goddes dignitee!
> Who dorste be so boold to disparage
> My doghter, that is come of swich lynage?'

Aleyn's suppressed excitement is brilliantly conveyed in action and in speech, by the repetitions as he shakes the sleeper ('thou John, thou swynes-heed, awak'), by his oaths, and by his delighted stress on 'swyved'. But even this is surpassed by the reply. Aleyn's speech ends halfway through a couplet, demanding the sleeper's attention; and the couplet is completed, to his astonishment and dismay, by the angry rumblings of the awakening miller, who comes to full consciousness with the rhyme-word 'hast?', and then breaks forth in thunder with 'A! false traitour!' Characteristically, Symkyn's reply springs from his pride and wrath; his daughter is not 'Malyne' but 'my doghter, that is come of swich lynage'.

There now begins the farcical battle which closes the story, and brings in John and the miller's wife (but not the daughter, for whom Chaucer has no further use). They do not awaken until the miller accidentally falls backwards on to their bed, for they are exhausted by their sport; and when the wife does awake (with surprised exclamations which she learnt in the nunnery), she continues in her error, and arouses John, supposing him her husband:

> 'Help, Symkyn, for the false clerkes fighte!'

No time is wasted in describing John's sensations:

> This John stirte up as faste as ever he myghte,
> And graspeth by the walles to and fro,
> To fynde a staf; and she stirte up also,
> And knew the estres bet than dide this John,
> And by the wal a staf she foond anon . . .

The miller's wife, it is plain, has by now discovered her mistake, and when she finds the staff it seems that the tide of battle will turn against the clerks; but by a final stroke of dramatic irony, her intervention turns the tide in their favour. She takes the miller's bald head for a nightcap worn by the clerk,

> And with the staf she drow ay neer and neer,
> And wende han hit this Aleyn at the fulle,
> And smoot the millere on the pyled skull.

This mistake, like the mistakes over the cradle, results from a very deliberate decision ('she drow ay neer and neer') based on wrong premises; and, as when Aleyn gets into bed not with John but with the miller, the outcome is stated with emphatic force and clinching rhyme. As for the mistake itself, it is made natural by Chaucer's earlier references to the miller's baldness ('As piled as an ape was his skulle'; 'Wel hath this millere vernysshed his heed').

Their enemy prostrate, the clerks rapidly take the road with the spoils of victory. They take nothing material but what is their own – their horse, their meal, their cake. Nevertheless, the miller has had losses and damage:

> Thus is the proude millere wel ybete,
> And hath ylost the gryndynge of the whete,
> And payed for the soper everideel
> Of Aleyn and of John, that bette hym weel.
> His wyf is swyved, and his doghter als.
> Lo, swich it is a millere to be fals!
> And therfore this proverbe is seyd ful sooth,
> 'Hym thar nat wene wel that yvele dooth';
> A gylour shal hymself bigyled be.
> And God, that sitteth heighe in magestee,
> Save al this compaignye, grete and smale!
> Thus have I quyt the Millere in my tale.

In these closing lines the Reeve reappears as narrator (during the tale we are conscious of no narrator but Chaucer); he lists with great satisfaction the points on which Symkyn has been worsted, sententiously underlines the moral of the story, and draws attention to his triumph over the pilgrim Miller. These are, for him, the important things to observe. For the Cook, however, who takes no particular interest in the Reeve's annoyance with the Miller, the moral is simply that it is dangerous to take in lodgers: 'Ne bryng nat every man into thyn hous'. And though it is obvious that the Cook has missed the main point, his misunderstanding reminds us that the tale's interest is not limited to the Reeve's attack on millers. We enjoy the poetic justice visited on Symkyn, but we equally enjoy the amusing opportunism of the clerks and the farcical mistakes of a night.

III *The Shipman's Tale*

The Shipman's Tale is about a merchant's wife who agrees with a monk that he shall lie with her in return for a hundred francs. The monk borrows the money from the merchant, completes his bargain with the wife, and later declines to repay the husband's money because the wife has already received it.

This tale is less admired by most readers than those of the Miller and the Reeve. This is partly because it is not so good a story, and partly because its telling has no dramatic consequences among the pilgrims. Though a merchant and a monk are unflatteringly portrayed, neither the pilgrim Merchant nor the pilgrim Monk shows indignation as does the Reeve after the Miller's tale of a carpenter.[1] The only comment is the Host's:

> 'Wel seyd, by *corpus dominus*', quod oure Hooste,
> 'Now longe moote thou saille by the cost,
> Sire gentil maister, gentil maryneer!
> God yeve the monk a thousand last quade yeer!
> A ha! felawes! beth ware of swich a jape!
> The monk putte in the mannes hood an ape,
> And in his wyves eek, by Seint Austyn!
> Draweth no monkes moore unto youre in.'

[1] This is the more noticeable since the monk of the story, like the pilgrim Monk, is an outrider (65), one who rides abroad looking after the abbey estates, and since the merchant of the story mentions merchants who feign a pilgrimage in order to avoid their creditors (233-234).

Likewise the tale does not spring inevitably from a dramatic situation. In the lines (called by Skeat *The Shipman's Prologue* and by Robinson *The Epilogue to the Man of Law's Tale*) which in some manuscripts precede *The Shipman's Tale*, the Shipman offers his tale merely as a means of warding off the sermon which the Host has ironically invited the Parson to give. The situation is itself a lively one, and the Shipman's simplicity in thinking that a sermon really will follow is amusing, besides conveniently stopping a quarrel from developing; but there is no reason why this tale rather than any other merry one should be told. Nor is there any reason why it should be told by the Shipman, and in fact only one manuscript makes him the speaker here, six naming the Summoner, and the rest most incongruously the Squire. Chaucer, then, may not have originally fixed on the Shipman as the teller of the tale, though the epilogue makes it clear that he later did so.

The Shipman's Tale is therefore virtually independent of its context. And just as Chaucer has done little to give it a context of dramatic speech and action, so he seems to have impressed his own artistic personality less upon this tale than upon his other comic ones. As usual, we have no direct source for the tale, but it is probable that it came from a lost French *fabliau* which supplied the setting in Saint-Denis, Bruges and Paris, as well as the outlines of the story. Chaucer neither naturalizes this story in an English setting, as he does the Miller's and the Reeve's, nor does he make any imaginative use of an exotic setting, as he uses Italy in *The Merchant's Tale*. The characters also are essentially the stock characters of farce: the merchant so preoccupied with his business that his wife's lover may court her under his nose, the unfaithful wife who offers her favours for sale, the opportunist monk who disregards his vow of chastity. Chaucer gives them life, of course, as he gives life to any character for whom he writes a speech; but the physical action, being virtually limited to the committing of adultery and the handing over of money, does not allow such characterization as the varied deceits and mistakes of the other farcical tales demand, nor the dramatic use of objects like tubs and ladders, shot-windows and hot ploughshares, hoppers and meal-troughs, horses, cradles, false keys and pear-trees. The interest for the reader accordingly lies in seeing what Chaucer is able to do with this somewhat elementary and intractable material.

He begins, as always, with his characters. His portrait of the merchant is perhaps the neatest miniature in *The Canterbury Tales*: the man's qualities are stated, and exhausted, in a couplet:

> A marchant whilom dwelled at Seint Denys,
> That riche was, for which men helde hym wys.

We learn more about the kind of folly he shows, as the story goes on, but we see at once that he is a fool at everything but buying and selling, a success as a merchant and a failure as a human being. The disposition of his wife, which the next couplet sums up almost as pithily, introduces the theme of the story, which is stated at some length and with some feeling:

> A wyf he hadde of excellent beautee;
> And compaignable and revelous was she,
> Which is a thyng that causeth more dispence
> Than worth is al the chiere and reverence
> That men hem doon at festes and at daunces.

Swiche salutaciouns and contenaunces
Passen as dooth a shadwe upon the wal;
But wo is hym that payen moot for al!
The sely housbonde, algate he moot paye,
He moot us clothe, and he moot us arraye,
Al for his owene worshipe richely,
In which array we daunce jolily.
And if that he noght may, par aventure,
Or ellis list no swich dispence endure,
But thynketh it is wasted and ylost,
Thanne moot another payen for oure cost,
Or lene us gold, and that is perilous.

There are two opinions of the lines beginning 'The sely housbonde'. One is that they were meant to be spoken by the Wife of Bath, that the tale was originally intended for her, and that they have been left unchanged by that same Chaucer who left the Man of Law telling the rhyme-royal tale of Custance after announcing that he would speak in prose, or who allowed the phrase 'unworthy sone of Eve' to stand in what is now *The Second Nun's Prologue*. The other opinion is that they are spoken dramatically by a masculine teller, who says, in effect, 'It is all very well for these women: they say, "Let our husbands, poor fools, pay our expenses or take the consequences" '. I do not think these two opinions necessarily contradict one another. Chaucer may have originally written the lines as part of a frank statement to be made by the Wife of Bath, but may afterwards have set them in a context which converted frankness into withering sarcasm. For if we consider the context, we must notice that the lines which go before 'The sely housbonde' could never have been meant for the Wife of Bath; the sentiments, as well as the pronoun ('hem'), are wrong, and it is hard to believe that Chaucer would add new material for a new (male) speaker without deleting or altering any old material for the old (female) speaker which immediately and incongruously followed. As for the lines beginning 'The sely housbonde', they certainly recall a passage in *The Wife of Bath's Prologue* (337-356); but in that passage the Wife is *quoting* the hostile opinions which she attributes to her old husbands. The passage in *The Shipman's Tale* is equally hostile to feminine extravagance, with the irritable sententiousness of

> Which is a thyng that causeth more dispence
> Than worth is al the chiere and reverence
> That men hem doon at festes and at daunces.

leading to the indignant outburst

> But wo is hym that payen moot for al!

and thence to the heavy sarcasm of

> The sely housbonde, algate he moot paye.

This opening is worth its length, and the time we have spent on it, because it is Chaucer's way of establishing our attitude towards his story. The hostility to feminine extravagance is the full-blown hostility of conventional satires on women, and we therefore anticipate a wholly conventional story of a cunning wife and a duped husband. Chaucer thus reserves the one surprise on which the story turns, namely the monk's trickery of the wife as well as of the husband.

Besides stating the theme of the story, he begins preparing for action:

. . . Thanne moot another payen for oure cost,
Or lene us gold, and that is perilous.

There is not only expense but danger, and 'perilous' colours the second line of the couplet and the sentence beginning there:

This noble marchaunt heeld a worthy hous,
For which he hadde alday so greet repair
For his largesse, and for his wyf was fair,
That wonder is; but herkneth to my tale.
Amonges alle his gestes, grete and smale,
Ther was a monk, a fair man and a boold –
I trowe a thritty wynter he was oold –
That evere in oon was drawynge to that place.

This monk's future relationship with the merchant's handsome wife is obvious, especially when he seems like one of the family –

. . . in his hous as famulier was he
As it is possible any freend to be –

and when he claims kindred with his 'cosyn' the merchant because they were born in the same village.

Thus been they knyt with eterne alliaunce,
And ech of hem gan oother for t'assure
Of bretherhede, whil that hir lyf may dure.

Sworn brotherhood is always regarded ironically by Chaucer, who knows well how men's plans are upset by inscrutable destiny or by natural selfishness, and whose irony varies according to his subject: the tragic romance of *The Knight's Tale*, the savage morality of *The Pardoner's Tale*, the farcical satire of *The Friar's Tale* and

The Summoner's Tale, the pure farce of *The Shipman's Tale*. The monk's calculated generosity to all the household, resulting in his useful popularity, is underlined by the apparently casual remark

> Na moore of this as now, for it suffiseth –

which implies that a word to the wise is enough, as well as that the characters are now going to be set in motion.

The merchant, 'on a day', makes ready to go on business to Bruges. This is like the carpenter's visits to Osney in *The Miller's Tale*, and we foresee the monk's courtship of the wife. Her husband not only fails to foresee it, but gives it unconscious encouragement in his invitation

> That he sholde come to Seint Denys to pleye
> With hym and with his wyf a day or tweye,
> Er he to Brugges went, in alle wise.

The monk duly arrives, with his usual presents; we hear the fatuous tones of the husband greeting him –

> Who was so welcome as my lord daun John,
> Oure deere cosyn, ful of curteisye? –

and the usual entertainment goes on:

> And thus I lete hem ete and drynke and pleye,
> This marchant and this monk, a day or tweye.

The couplet repeats the merchant's invitation, with this difference, that there is no mention of the wife. What is she doing and planning? The next part of the story allows us to find out, but not immediately.

The thridde day, this marchant up ariseth,
And on his nedes sadly hym avyseth,
And up into his countour-hous gooth he,
To rekene with hymself, as wel may be,
Of thilke yeer, how that it with hym stood,
And how that he despended hadde his good,
And if that he encressed were or noon.
His bookes and his bagges many oon
He leith biforn hym on his countyng-bord.
Ful riche was his tresor and his hord,
For which ful faste his countour-dore he shette;
And eek he nolde that no man sholde hym lette
Of his acountes, for the meene tyme;
And thus he sit til it was passed pryme.

We are expecting him to be off, so that Daun John can seduce his wife, and we are meant to grow impatient of this detailed account of his methodical and self-important proceedings. The account also makes him a real merchant (not a mere farce-figure whose occupation is only a means of getting him out of the way), and gives material existence to the money which will be needed later in the story. But its main importance is to reveal character and situation. The merchant's prudence, and its limitations, are summed up when he locks himself in with his treasure and leaves his wife at large outside. For he is not the only one stirring:

Daun John was rysen in the morwe also,
And in the gardyn walketh to and fro,
And hath his thynges seyd ful curteisly.
This goode wyf cam walkynge pryvely
Into the gardyn, there he walketh softe,
And hym saleweth, as she hath doon ofte.

All this is heavy with suggestion. The meeting is not exactly an assignation, yet it is not an ordinary meeting either. The 'mayde child', who comes with the wife, is used by her as a sort of innocent *chaperone*, adding piquancy to a situation which she is too young to understand, and which in any case the wife can forbid her to reveal. Nevertheless, she seems superfluous, for the mood of the meeting is clear enough without her, and at its end she has simply vanished.

The conversation between the wife and the monk is a long one, and undoubtedly one reason for its length is that Chaucer must clothe the bare bones of his story. Nicholas wins Alison in thirty-five lines. Daun John's bargain with the merchant's wife takes just six times as long to accomplish. Chaucer uses the long dialogue to show the caution and subtlety of both parties, who are slow to declare their real relationship towards each other, though both are well aware of it, as appears from their very conscious use of 'cosyn' and 'nece', and from Daun John's covert and joking hints at the true subject of their talk;

> 'O deere cosyn myn, daun John', she sayde,
> 'What eyleth yow so rathe for to ryse?'
> 'Nece', quod he, 'it oghte ynough suffise
> Fyve houres for to slepe upon a nyght,
> But it were for an old appalled wight,
> As been thise wedded men, that lye and dare
> As in a fourme sit a wery hare,
> Were al forstraught with houndes grete and smale.
> But deere nece, why be ye so pale?
> I trowe, certes, that oure goode man
> Hath yow laboured sith the nyght bigan,
> That yow were nede to resten hastily.'

And with that word he lough ful murily,
And of his owene thought he wax al reed.

Daun John enlivens his unctuous reply (that an ascetic needs little sleep) with a witty contrast between the celibate and that stock figure of satire the old husband who cannot satisfy his wife's sexual appetite. From this 'old appalled wight' it is an easy leap to the personal question 'But deere nece, why be ye so pale?' ('Speaking of pallid old men, you look pale yourself' – the line puts a heavy stress on 'ye'), and to the even more personal conclusion. Daun John merrily pretends to think that it is the wife, not her husband, who is exhausted by the business of the marriage bed; but his real purpose is perhaps to make her declare her dissatisfaction with her husband's labours there. His sudden blush, at least, makes his unspoken desires perfectly clear, and also, after his talk of the pallor of satiety, suggests his appetite for the merchant's wife.

She is quick to respond, hinting at inexpressible griefs and threatening melodramatic actions, exile and even suicide. Daun John takes his cue, and stares on her in earnest amazement; very much the father-confessor, he bids her put away these dreadful thoughts, offers counsel or help (we foresee of what practical nature), and vows secrecy. All this is consistent enough with his profession, but when she replies by extravagantly swearing, in her turn, on his breviary, never to reveal anything that *he* may tell *her*, she is obviously encouraging him to make love to her. A laconic comment shows what kind of understanding is growing between them:

Thus been they sworn, and heerupon they kiste,
And ech of hem tolde oother what hem liste.

The kiss is outwardly one of agreement, and her protest that she acts from 'love and affiance' is just capable of an honest interpretation, but both are ambiguous, and the wife now harps upon the word 'cosyn' so as to drive the monk into a hearty declaration of love (he swears it on his monastic vow, which of course included chastity):

'Nay', quod this monk, 'by God and seint Martyn,
He is na moore cosyn unto me
Than is this leef that hangeth on the tree!
I clepe hym so, by Seint Denys of Fraunce,
To have the moore cause of acqueyntaunce
Of yow, which I have loved specially
Aboven alle wommen, sikerly.
This swere I yow on my professioun.
Telleth your grief, lest that he come adoun;
And hasteth yow, and gooth youre wey anon.'
'My deere love', quod she, 'O my daun John . . .'

This completes the preliminary skirmish, but the lovers must now go on to their bargain. Chaucer has already made it clear that the merchant is safe in his counting-house and will not interrupt them (for there is no merit in arousing expectations that will not be fulfilled); yet he skilfully punctuates their long conversation by the monk's fear of being interrupted; and by means of this fear, he brings the wife to the point.

The request for a hundred francs, on which the story depends, comes as a surprise to us. The long preamble, and the wife's reluctance to reveal the privacies of her married life ('Neither abedde, ne in noon other place'), have prepared us for talk of love and not of money. It is, indeed, questionable whether the wife really desires Daun John at all; perhaps she merely makes use of his desire for her. If so, there is an amusing fitness in her thinking to use him for her own convenience, only to find at last that he has used her for his.

The wife needs the hundred francs to pay for clothes she has bought, and declares in her melodramatic way that her husband will have her life if he catches her in debt, and that she would rather die than suffer 'sclaundre or vileynye'; yet she implies clearly enough the scandalous repayment that Daun John may have if only he will 'lend' her the money:

> 'For at a certeyn day I wol yow paye,
> And doon to yow what plesance and service
> That I may doon, right as yow list devise.'

And 'this gentil monk' at once takes her meaning; calling her no longer 'nece' but 'myn owene lady deere', he promises to bring the hundred francs when her husband is safely on his journey. The kiss now is of a different character from their earlier one:

> And with that word he caughte hire by the flankes,
> And hire embraceth harde, and kiste hire ofte.
> 'Gooth now youre wey', quod he, 'al stille and softe,
> And lat us dyne as soone as that ye may;
> For by my chilyndre it is pryme of day.
> Gooth now, and beeth as trewe as I shal be.'

Daun John's glance at his dial may perhaps suggest that now he has concluded the bargain he would rather have his dinner than any more of the wife's conversation, and it may thus foreshadow his unscrupulous treatment of her; but its obvious use is to bring the merchant back into the story.

The wife, discarding her melodramatic miseries, goes off 'as jolif as a pye', orders dinner, and knocks 'boldely' at the door of the counting-house, as if she had nothing to conceal. She can name Daun John without a blush, and can use his name as a magic charm upon her blindly partial husband. Clearly she is not overawed by the man whom she can address thus:

'What, sire, how longe wol ye faste?
How longe tyme wol ye rekene and caste
Youre sommes, and youre bookes, and youre thynges?
The devel have part on alle swiche rekenynges!'

And the merchant's reply, complacent, sententious and calm, shows that they have been through this dialogue many a time. He patronizes her weak understanding of his mystery –

'Wyf', quod this man, 'litel kanstow devyne
The curious bisynesse that we have . . .'

and justifies his prudence:

'And therfore have I greet necessitee
Upon this queynte world t'avyse me;
For everemoore we moote stonde in drede
Of hap and fortune in oure chapmanhede.'

His self-importance makes us eager to see him proved a fool, and his last couplet reminds us that he ought to stand in dread of fortune in his private affairs as well as those of his business. After this, his directions to his wife, about her behaviour in his absence, are full of unconscious irony: she is to be pliant and agreeable to all, and take great care of the household goods. We are, of course, thinking all the time of her bargain with Daun John, and of her pressing need for the hundred francs:

> 'Thee lakketh noon array ne no vitaille;
> Of silver in thy purs shaltow nat faille.'
> And with that word his countour-dore he shette . . .

From this significant end to the conversation we pass straight to the dinner. Again there is no important action between this dialogue and the next; Chaucer must simply do the best he can, so he makes the dinner comic by showing it in quick motion:

> But hastily a messe was ther seyd,
> And spedily the tables were yleyd,
> And to the dyner faste they hem spedde,
> And richely this monk the chapman fedde.

After the dinner, Daun John takes his 'cosyn' aside, and is full of good advice and good wishes for his journey, protesting that he is ready to do him any good turn he cares to name. All this is mildly comic now that we know the monk's real feelings of indifference and contempt, but with his next word the full farcical situation bursts upon us:

> 'O thyng, er that ye goon, if it may be,
> I wolde prey yow; for to lene me
> An hundred frankes, for a wyke or tweye,
> For certein beestes that I moste beye . . .'

Daun John's position as an 'officer' of his monastery is thus turned to useful account, and the topic of buying beasts is somehow suggestive of his real intentions. The merchant, who is more liberal to his 'cosyn' than to his wife, eagerly complies:

> 'Now sikerly this is a smal requeste.
> My gold is youres, whan that it yow leste,
> And nat oonly my gold, but my chaffare.
> Take what yow list, God shilde that ye spare.'

But his business sense not completely deserting him, he reminds the monk that the money will have to be repaid at some convenient future date. Accordingly, we are not surprised by the ensuing complications about its repayment later in the story. As is there made clear, the merchant is so besotted upon his 'cosyn' that he never intended to ask for repayment; but if the money were an outright gift, then only the husband would be fooled, not the wife also. Chaucer, needless to say, must firmly state that the wife knows nothing of this, Daun John's second bargain –

> No wight in al this world wiste of this loone,
> Savynge this marchant and daun John allone –

but he leaves his statement general, so that we can work out for ourselves how this second bargain is connected with the first.

Daun John returns to his abbey that same day (thus avoiding any suspicion of wishing to stay with the wife after her husband's departure); and next morning the merchant duly sets off for Bruges, where we leave him absorbed in his affairs, in his prudent way, doing nothing rash – or interesting:

> Now goth this marchant faste and bisily
> Aboute his nede, and byeth and creaunceth.
> He neither pleyeth at the dees ne daunceth,

But as a marchaunt, shortly for to telle,
He let his lyf, and there I lete hym dwelle.

The Sonday next the marchant was agon,
To Seint Denys ycomen is daun John,
With crowne and berd al fressh and newe yshave.

Though the monk's return is evidently a few days after the merchant's departure, the poetic effect is one of stage farce: the unsuspecting cuckold ambles off the stage in one direction, and the bold seducer swaggers in from the other. The effect is to be repeated in reverse almost immediately, for the monk's business with the wife is rapidly dispatched. The sketch of the dapper Daun John, 'with crowne and berd al fressh and newe yshave', is not only vivid and realistic (Chaucer remembers that a monk's crown as well as his beard needs regular shaving), but also illustrates the monk's character (he is smooth and plausible) and wittily comments on it (the tonsure, which he smartens up in order to look handsome in the wife's eyes, is the symbol of his monastic vows). The wife agrees to lie with him 'for thise hundred frankes' – Chaucer thus reminds us that these very coins are her husband's –

And this acord parfourned was in dede.
In myrthe al nyght a bisy lyf they lede
Til it was day, that daun John wente his way,
And bad the meynee, 'farewel, have good day!'

The merchant now re-enters the scene, returning home from his journey. He tells his wife that his business has been successful, but that he needs some ready money, 'twenty thousand sheeld', to settle a debt he has incurred in buying merchandise:

For which this marchant is to Parys gon
To borwe of certeine freendes that he hadde
A certeyn frankes; and somme with him he ladde.

We do not at first connect his need for 'twenty thousand sheeld' with the previous events, but as soon as the sum is converted into francs the connexion is clear, and we foresee that while he is in Paris he will visit Daun John at the abbey. And indeed he goes straight to Daun John, though his object is not to recover his loan but to show friendship and incidentally to boast of his business success (this to Daun John, who is the best business-man in the story). His talk of money naturally leads him to say why he is in Paris, which in its turn allows Daun John to bring up the topic of the hundred francs: he would lend the merchant the whole 'twenty thousand sheeld', if he had it, as a friendly return for the merchant's recent loan to him – a loan which, by the way, he has already repaid:

'But nathelees, I took unto oure dame
Youre wyf, at hom, the same gold ageyn
Upon youre bench; she woot it wel, certeyn,
By certeyn tokenes that I kan hire telle.'

With this statement, literally and therefore comically true ('the same gold ageyn'), Daun John takes his leave, for he is conveniently going out of town with the abbot. His last words in the story recall the theme of 'cosynage':

'Grete wel oure dame, myn owene nece sweete,
And fare wel, deere cosyn, til we meete!'

He has deceived his accomplice the wife as well as his dupe the husband. His relationship with her has been closer than cousinly (though the merchant will never know how close), and yet she will not think of him with affection when she learns that the hundred francs he gave her had been borrowed by him from her husband, to whom therefore she ought to be able to return them.

The merchant, meanwhile, having completed his own borrowings and paid off his debt, leaving himself in expectation of a handsome profit, returns in triumph to his wife. He is 'murie as a papejay', and his exhilaration expresses itself in sexual energy:

His wyf ful redy mette hym atte gate,
As she was wont of oold usage algate,
And al that nyght in myrthe they bisette;
For he was riche and cleerly out of dette.
Whan it was day, this marchant gan embrace
His wyf al newe, and kiste hir on hir face,
And up he gooth and maketh it ful tough.
'Namoore', quod she, 'by God, ye have ynough!'
And wantownly agayn with hym she pleyde . . .

This is the situation when, characteristically mixing business with pleasure, the merchant mildly reproves his wife for having

'. . . maad a manere straungenesse
Bitwixen me and my cosyn daun John'

(nothing to the estrangement there would be if he knew the whole truth), by not mentioning the monk's repayment of the borrowed hundred francs; he is afraid that his talk of borrowing offended Daun John, and insists with absurd pathos that he never intended to reclaim his money (showing a ridiculously delicate concern for the feelings of his deceiver). He begs his wife to tell him, in future,

'If any dettour hath in myn absence
Ypayed thee, lest thurgh thy necligence
I myghte hym axe a thyng that he hath payed.'

This remark gains extra comic force from the fact that the sexual intercourse of man and wife is conventionally described as their mutual debt.[1] Daun Juan has not only repaid to the wife his own debt to her husband, he has in this figurative sense paid her husband's debt to her also.

This secondary meaning of 'debt' is thrust upon us, partly by the conversation's taking place in bed, and partly by the clever way in which the wife now gets herself out of her difficulty. She is naturally, and comically, taken aback by the monk's perfidy –

'Marie, I deffie the false monk, daun John!' –

but with her ready wit and shamelessness she answers 'boldely' that she imagined the money to be a personal gift

'For cosynage, and eek for beele cheere
That he hath had ful ofte tymes heere';

a plausible reply, which also reminds us that the money was indeed the monk's payment for pleasures afforded him at his 'cosyn's' house. She then humorously proposes a mutually satisfactory compromise:

'Ye han mo slakkere dettours than am I!
For I wol paye yow wel and redily
Fro day to day, and if so be I faille,
I am youre wyf; score it upon my taille,

[1] See, for example, *The Merchant's Tale*, 2048, and Robinson's note; also *The Parson's Tale*, 940-941, and *The Wife of Bath's Prologue*, 130, 153.

And I shal paye as soone as ever I may.
For by my trouthe, I have on myn array,
And nat on wast, bistowed every deel;
And for I have bistowed it so weel
For youre honour, for Goddes sake, I seye,
As be nat wrooth, but lat us laughe and pleye;
Ye shal my joly body have to wedde;
By God, I wol nat paye yow but abedde!
Forgyve it me, myn owene spouse deere;
Turne hiderward, and maketh bettre cheere.'

The merchant sees that complaint is useless, 'sith that the thyng may nat amended be'; he is thinking of his money, 'wasted and ylost' (for he does not appreciate his wife's nice distinction between wasting money and spending it on clothes), and is unaware that something else beyond remedy has happened, so that his forgiveness of her, and his friendly warning 'Keep bet my good, this yeve I thee in charge', are unconsciously ironical.

Chaucer's conclusion, where the wife ingeniously escapes from the difficult situation in which the monk has placed her, differs from the conclusion in the closest analogues, the stories of Boccaccio and of Sercambi.[1] In both these versions, the wife is compelled to return the money to her husband, and her false lover's trick becomes a just punishment for her covetousness. In Chaucer's version, on the contrary, though the chief winner is of course the monk (as the Host's appreciative remarks make plain), the tale ends with a minor triumph on the part of the wife, and with the punning couplet

Thus endeth now my tale, and God us sende
Taillynge ynough unto oure lyves ende.

[1] Printed in *Sources and Analogues*, pp. 441-446.

This couplet takes up the line in the wife's speech, 'I am youre wyf; score it upon my taille', and provides, in my opinion, a much better reason for ascribing the tale originally to the Wife of Bath than do the early lines about 'the sely housbonde'. For the concluding lines of the tales are often personal (the Reeve, the Friar, and the Wife of Bath herself spring to mind); and whereas there is no apparent reason for the Shipman's (or any man's) praying for a lifetime of such 'taillynge', there is every reason why the Wife of Bath should speak for all wives in her desire to score up extravagant debts for clothing and make no payment but in the marriage-bed. The speeches of the merchant's wife in this story, indeed, sometimes recall the Wife of Bath's own emphatic style:

> 'How longe tyme wol ye rekene and caste
> Your sommes, and your bookes, and your thynges?
> The devel have part on alle swich rekenynges!'
>
> 'By God, I wol nat paye yow but abedde!'

and at other times make use of her subject-matter, as when the wife interrupts her complaint to the monk with the generalization

> 'And wel ye woot that wommen naturelly
> Desiren thynges sixe as wel as I:
> They wolde that hir housbondes sholde be
> Hardy and wise, and riche, and therto free,
> And buxom unto his wyf, and fressh abedde.'

It may be that Chaucer contemplated giving this tale to the Wife of Bath at one time, and then changed his mind, partly because he found that the character in the story was too like the story-teller, and partly because, for all her final ingenuity, the merchant's wife comes off only second-best. Certainly the Wife of Bath's present tale is much better suited to her: it illustrates her general ideal, that wives should have dominion over their husbands, while the fact that it is a magic romance and not a farce leaves room for the contrast of her frankly autobiographical prologue, where she shows how she realized this ideal in her own marriages.

Chaucer's plans, however, must remain a matter of speculation, and I am not suggesting that he ended his tale with the wife's resourcefulness for the special purpose of fitting it to the Wife of Bath as teller. He may have found this end to the story in some lost *fabliau*, or he may have invented it because he preferred it to the final moralistic defeat of the wife in the analogues. For whatever reason he introduced it, the wife's successful bargain with her husband – the third bargain – brings the story to a satisfying end; we receive surprise and pleasure from her humorous retort, and this dialogue in bed gives both husband and wife a comic reality which develops from their earlier dialogue in the counting-house, and looks forward to the reality of the Wife of Bath and her husbands.

But though the end is a satisfying one for this story, the story itself is less satisfying than Chaucer's other completed comic ones, with the exception of *The Canon's Yeoman's Tale*, which has no true plot but merely narrates a series of rogueries practised by a sham alchemist on a gullible priest (the Yeoman's autobiographical disclosures are much more interesting than his tale). This is not to say that mere thinness of plot is enough to make a comic tale unsatisfactory: *The Summoner's Tale* has a thin plot but has never lacked admirers.

The Shipman's Tale has a sound farcical plot but one which lacks both the physical action and the downright improbability necessary to great farce. This is why the conversations, despite their interest and liveliness, seem like Chaucer's compensations for the story's shortcomings: he cannot give us action, so he gives us talk, and the tale remains somewhat bodiless. It is not long, yet it might be shorter without much loss.[1] Likewise, though Chaucer tells the story in such a way as to bring out every comic feature of its situations, the situations themselves are of limited variety, and the climax, being wholly an intellectual one, is not comparable with the fantastic actions which dramatically conclude the Miller's tale or the Reeve's, and which Chaucer has made not only plausible but inevitable.

[1] There are also signs that Chaucer has not revised this tale as carefully as some of his others. For example, there are tautologies (12, 'He moot us clothe, and he moot us arraye'; 400, 'This wyf was nat afered nor affrayed') and repetitions (319-320, 'Til it was day, that daun John wente his way,/ And bad the meynee, "farewel, have good day!" '; 358-359, 'she woot it wel, certeyn,/ By certeyn tokenes that I kan hire telle'). Unconnected statements are roughly soldered together by conjunctions (173, 'And wel ye woot . . .'; 178, 'But by that ilke Lord . . .'). The same rhyme is used for two couplets with only one other couplet intervening (29-30, 33-34).

IV *The Nun's Priest's Tale*

The Nun's Priest's Tale of the cock and the fox is the most widely known of Chaucer's comic tales, and is universally agreed to rank among his best. Perhaps in no other tale is Chaucer so constantly present, showing us his shrewd understanding of human nature and at the same time his genial tolerance of human frailty; his keen sense of the ridiculous; his well-stored mind; and his deceptively easy narrative manner, seeming to digress without premeditation, yet being in perfect control of his story all the time.

The story itself is a very simple one, wholly lacking in the complications of the Miller's and the Reeve's. Reduced to its essentials, it is an elementary but very satisfying reversal of a situation. First the fox flatters the cock into becoming his prey, and then the cock in his turn flatters the fox into releasing him; the cock shuts his eyes when he should keep them open, the fox opens his mouth when he should keep it shut.

Chaucer's habit, as we have already seen, is not to reduce a story to its essentials, but rather to give it as much elaboration as is consistent with keeping its outline clear. In *The Shipman's Tale*, where he has a simple story, he has the difficult task of amplifying without the opportunity of digressing or indulging in description. The story of *The Nun's Priest's Tale*, on the contrary, gives him far more liberty. He can in fact digress from his story before it has properly begun at all. Before the fox appears on the scene, Chauntecleer's prophetic dream allows an elaborate discussion to take place between husband and wife on the causes and value of dreams; and before the fox begins speaking to the cock, Chaucer reflects philosophically on destiny and cynically on the danger of following women's advice. As for description, Chauntecleer is brilliantly portrayed at the outset, and is given the kind of heroic simile that is in the serious tales bestowed on a Palamon:

> He looketh as it were a grym leoun.

All these are means whereby Chaucer inflates the fable on which his story is based.

The epic treatment itself, and many of its details (such as Chauntecleer's dream), are things which Chaucer has borrowed, either directly or indirectly, from the *Roman de Renard*.[1] Nevertheless, Chaucer handles his material very freely, partly because such freedom was natural to him, as it was to Shakespeare, and partly because he was writing a story complete in itself, not an episode in a larger work. The commentary in particular is all his own.

He makes Chauntecleer the hero of his tale. Honours are even at the end, but the course of the story engages our sympathy for him in his capture, and our admiration for his ready wit in his escape. Much of the tale is devoted to displaying his character, making us interested in his fate, and showing at an early stage the vanity that is nearly his downfall. We have to bear in mind that his vanity is essential to the story, making him susceptible

[1] On the relationship of *The Nun's Priest's Tale* to the *Roman* and to other works, see Kenneth Sisam's valuable introduction to his edition of the tale (Oxford, 1927). The episode of the *Roman* is printed in *Sources and Analogues*, pp. 646-658.

to the fox's flattery; and therefore, though the story is a moral one, and we are invited to mark the moral at the end, we must not give too much weight to Chauntecleer's failings, or we shall be in danger of reading the Nun's Priest's tale as though it were the Monk's.[1]

By making this tale follow the Monk's, Chaucer has in fact at one stroke put his readers into the right mood for it. The Monk's tragic narratives of the falls of princes have harped on a single string, relating

> that Fortune alwey wole assaille
> With unwar strook the regnes that been proude,

and the theme has become unbearable to everyone, Knight, Host, pilgrims and readers alike:

> Youre tale anoyeth al this compaignye.

The courteous Knight begs for comedy, comedy in its widest sense, the contrary of tragedy, a story with a happy ending instead of a sad one, a story where the hero succeeds instead of failing. As for the Host, he bluntly condemns as sterile this 'tragedie', where what is done cannot be undone. He calls on the Nun's Priest for what is wanted –

> Telle us swich thyng as may oure hertes glade –

and the Nun's Priest agrees:

> But I be myrie, ywis I wol be blamed.

[1] See, for example, David Holbrook's essay, in B. Ford (ed.), *A Guide to English Literature. I. The Age of Chaucer*, 1952, pp. 118-128: 'Chauntecleer is Adam . . . and the col-fox, black-tipped, is the Devil. . . . The farmyard chase at the end is, in its own way, the moral confusion following the Fall of Man' (pp. 122-123). This moralistic approach is not only inconsistent with the tale's whole spirit, but with its events too, when Chauntecleer cleverly plays on the fox's vanity and (to our delight) escapes the consequences of his folly.

His ensuing tale is a comic one in every way. It ends happily, with Chauntecleer safe and sound, and it is told with wit and humour. Yet it is not merely a relief from the Monk's (as any merry tale would have been), but is a most satisfying contrast, because in applying the full dignity of tragedy to the fate of Chauntecleer it becomes burlesque, of the highest order. We find here the continuity which is typical of Chaucer at his best, as when the Miller's tale follows the Knight's, and the Reeve's follows the Miller's. It is surely no accident that the last story which the Monk is allowed to tell is that of Croesus, whose foreboding dream prepares us for Chauntecleer's.

Chaucer, however, does not plunge into the tale of Chauntecleer and the fox without due preparation.

> A povre wydwe, somdeel stape in age,
> Was whilom dwellyng in a narwe cotage
> Biside a grove, stondynge in a dale.
> This wydwe, of which I telle yow my tale,
> Syn thilke day that she was last a wyf,
> In pacience ladde a ful symple lyf,
> For litel was hir catel and hir rente.
> By housbondrie of swich as God hire sente
> She foond hirself and eek hir doghtren two.
> Thre large sowes hadde she, and namo,
> Three keen, and eek a sheep that highte Malle.
> Ful sooty was hire bour and eek hir halle,
> In which she eet ful many a sklendre meel.
> Of poynaunt sauce hir neded never a deel.
> No deyntee morsel passed thurgh hir throte;
> Hir diete was accordant to hir cote.
> Repleccioun ne made hire nevere sik;
> Attempree diete was al hir phisik,

And exercise, and hertes suffisaunce.
The goute lette hire nothyng for to daunce,
N'apoplexie shente nat hir heed.
No wyn ne drank she, neither whit ne reed;
Hir bord was served moost with whit and blak,
Milk and broun breed, in which she foond no lak,
Seynd bacoun, and somtyme an ey or tweye;
For she was, as it were, a maner deye.

This is like the opening of *The Reeve's Tale*, an introduction to the setting (the grove is that from which the fox is to emerge) and to the persons. But Chaucer makes it clear, in spite of the line

This wydwe, of which I telle yow my tale,

that the widow and her two daughters (who are already brought in, to take part in the chase at the end of the story) are not to play an active part like Symkyn and his family. In the first place, they have no names; but the sheep, Malle, has this mark of personality, and we are thus prepared to hear about Chauntecleer and Pertelote and Daun Russell. Secondly, they have no interesting idiosyncrasy such as the crafty dissimulation which announces the nameless summoner of *The Friar's Tale* as the central character of that story. Modern commentators, particularly those who dwell on Chauntecleer's pride and sensuality, are apt to idealize this widow as representing simplicity and goodness and 'the plain human life which exists underneath the graces and trappings of cultivated life, and beside which man's theories of life must be set.'[1] But though Chaucer has

[1] Holbrook, p. 120. Chauntecleer's dream 'was a supernatural warning of his evil state of soul' (p. 123). The most extreme allegorists identify the widow with the Church: see *The Year's Work in English Studies*, XXXIV (for 1953), p. 68; XXXV (for 1954), p. 62.

kindly feelings towards her (as he has for that other old widow in *The Friar's Tale*), he is at present concerned not to point a moral but to adorn a tale. She is not Piers Plowman, nor is meant to be. Her simple life is presented for our casual approval but not as a standard of behaviour. It does not attract our full attention. It is described mostly in negatives; and these are not the strong negatives, implying bad behaviour in others, with which Chaucer describes the Parson (who did not leave his sheep in the mire while he ran to Saint Paul's in search of a sinecure), but rather the humorous negatives with which he describes the merchant's sober life at Bruges in *The Shipman's Tale* ('He neither pleyeth at the dees ne daunceth'). Her health is due to her temperance; her temperance, to her poverty.

> The goute lette hire nothyng for to daunce,
> N'apoplexie shente nat hir heed.
> No wyn ne drank she, neither whit ne reed;
> Hir bord was served moost with whit and blak,
> Milk and broun breed . . .

We are, in short, quite as aware of Chaucer the humorist as we are aware of the widow, whom we may even call a part of the setting for Chauntecleer, since the details of her simple fare serve once again to direct us towards the farmyard animals: milk (from her cows), bacon (from her pigs), 'and somtyme an ey or tweye' (from the seven hens of whom we have yet to hear).

From her fenced yard surrounded by a dry ditch, Chauntecleer emerges in all his splendour, a splendour heightened by his contrast with the drab widow. She is described in negatives, he in hyperboles and superlatives.

In al the land of crowyng nas his peer.
His voys was murier than the murie orgon
On messe-dayes that in the chirche gon.
Wel sikerer was his crowyng in his logge
Than is a clokke or an abbey orlogge.
By nature he knew ech ascencioun
Of the equynoxial in thilke toun;
For whan degrees fiftene weren ascended,
Thanne crew he, that it myghte nat been amended.
His coomb was redder than the fyn coral,
And batailled as it were a castel wal;
His byle was blak, and as the jeet it shoon;
Lyk asure were his legges and his toon;
His nayles whitter than the lylye flour,
And lyk the burned gold was his colour.

Chaucer's employment of simile is usually so restrained and modest that portraits like those of Alison (in *The Miller's Tale*) and of Chauntecleer dazzle the reader. We recognize, in this tale at least, that the chief character is being presented. As in some mediaeval illuminations, the cock is drawn on a bigger scale than the woman who tends him.[1] Her placid mediocrity is a foil to his extravagance. Nevertheless, as a human being, she is present in the background to make his extravagance continually ridiculous. His heroic world is bounded by her stick fence and dry ditch. Chaucer could not have given us this sense of proportion – on which our enjoyment of his later comic disproportion depends – if he had begun with the cock and hen instead of with the widow.

Without actually mentioning that Chauntecleer is vain

[1] See, for example, G. M. Trevelyan's *English Social History*, illustrated edition, Volume I (1949), plate 26.

of his appearance and accomplishments (his crowing, so important later), Chaucer suggests as much, partly by describing him with excessive admiration, and also by bringing in the seven hens as his devoted satellites:

> This gentil cok hadde in his governaunce
> Sevene hennes for to doon all his plesaunce.

Furthermore, by way of the hens, Chaucer can begin his story (which in the *Roman* begins with the fox entering the yard) with Chauntecleer's dream. And the dream, besides foreshadowing the course of the tale –

> 'I saugh a beest
> Was lyk an hound, and wolde han maad areest
> Upon my body, and wolde han had me deed' –

brings in the fox as a worthy enemy of Chauntecleer; he is quite as vividly, if more realistically, drawn;

> 'His colour was bitwixe yelow and reed,
> And tipped was his tayl and bothe his eeris
> With blak, unlyk the remenant of his heeris;
> His snowte smal, with glowynge eyen tweye.'

We have all seen a fox, so that there would be no point in describing him when he enters the action ('a col-fox . . . the same nyght thurghout the hegges brast / Into the yerd'); but since Chauntecleer has never seen one, the description here is dramatic and trembles with the speaker's anxiety:

> 'Yet of his look for feere almoost I deye.'[1]

[1] If Chaucer was working directly from the *Roman*, he chose not to follow it in making Chauntecleer's dream take the form of being put in a red fur garment with a narrow bone neck, an obvious allegory of being eaten by a fox. As in *The Reeve's Tale*, Chaucer's treatment is free of the unnecessary elaboration and mystification of the French version.

Chauntecleer's dream, and his consequent dialogue with Pertelote, occupy a great part of the tale, and Chaucer makes the most of his opportunity. The course of the dialogue is so familiar that we often overlook Chaucer's stroke of comic genius in relating Pertelote's argument to the story in general and to Chauntecleer's dream in particular: dreams come from physical disorder, physical disorder comes from abundance of humours, humours have their distinctive colours, and so a *red* animal explains away the whole thing! We cannot, however, miss the relish with which Chaucer develops Chauntecleer's counter-argument that dreams are true prophecies. The 'examples' with which this argument is supported give full play to his narrative powers (which he has had little chance to use as yet), besides allowing him to strike a deeper note than this light-hearted story elsewhere permits;

> And so bifel that, longe er it were day,
> This man mette in his bed, ther as he lay,
> How that his felawe gan upon hym calle,
> And seyde, 'Allas! for in an oxes stalle
> This nyght I shal be mordred ther I lye.
> Now help me, deere brother, or I dye.
> In alle haste com to me!' he sayde.
> This man out of his sleep for feere abrayde . . .

The emphasis of this appeal is very poignant. In the other 'example', that of the shipwreck, the scoffing speech of the sceptical traveller ('Men dreme of thyng that nevere was ne shal') is, in its different mood, equally convincing. And the voices of the disputants themselves, of course, are also continually breaking through, so that we do not mind the story's standing still, because we never feel that it is becoming a mere vehicle for the digressions:

> 'Madame', quod he, 'graunt mercy of youre loore.
> But nathelees, as touchyng daun Catoun,
> That hath of wysdom swich a greet renoun,
> Though that he bad no dremes for to drede,
> By God, men may in olde bookes rede
> Of many a man moore of auctorite
> Than evere Caton was, so moot I thee,
> That al the revers seyn of this sentence . . .'

These are the tones of the husband asserting his intellectual supremacy, while Pertolote's practical advice about medicine displays not only her care for her husband's health but also her desire to manage him:

> 'A day or two ye shul have digestyves
> Of wormes, er ye take youre laxatyves . . .'

Moreover, since the outcome proves Chauntecleer right and Pertelote wrong in this instance,[1] Chaucer is already preparing to bring in his own later observations on women's advice:

> Wommennes conseils been ful ofte colde;
> Wommannes conseil broghte us first to wo,
> And made Adam fro Paradys to go,
> Ther as he was ful myrie and wel at ese.
> But for I noot to whom it myght displese,

[1] Contrast the *Roman*, where it is the hen who interprets the dream correctly and the cock who disregards it. It is worth noting that Chaucer, though he says that Chauntecleer 'tok his conseil of his wyf', is too good a judge of character to allow him to admit himself infiuenced by her arguments or by her contempt for his cowardice. Chauntecleer insists that he will have adversity, but maintains that his love for Pertelote gives him spirit enough to ignore his visionary warning.

If I conseil of wommen wolde blame,
Passe over, for I seyde it in my game.
Rede auctours, where they trete of swich mateere,
And what they seyn of wommen ye may heere.
Thise been the cokkes wordes, and nat myne;
I kan noon harm of no womman divyne.

These lines may, of course, be taken as the Nun's Priest's (spoken with a side-glance at the Prioress), but even if this be a correct interpretation it does not prevent their being also Chaucer's.[1] They put the narrator fully in touch with his readers – or listeners, if we think of Chaucer reading aloud to a court audience – and they thus serve the same purpose as those conscious incongruities by which he keeps reminding us that he is making animals and birds behave like human beings for his pleasure and ours:

For thilke tyme, as I have understonde,
Beestes and briddes koude speke and synge.

Curteys she was, discreet, and debonaire,
And compaignable, and bar hyrself so faire,
Syn thilke day that she was seven nyght oold,
That trewely she hath the herte in hoold
Of Chauntecleer, loken in every lith.

'Have ye no mannes herte, and han a berd?'

'By God! I hadde levere than my sherte
That ye hadde rad his legende, as have I.'

[1] My own opinion, like Sisam's (p. xlii), is that in reading the tale one is nowhere conscious of the Nun's Priest's personality and everywhere conscious of Chaucer's.

'For whan I se the beautee of youre face,
Ye been so scarlet reed aboute youre yen,
It maketh al my drede for to dyen.'

With the end of the dispute, and the coming of dawn, the story is ready to move forward; and so Chauntecleer flies down from the beam into the yard, where he struts fearlessly about 'in al his pryde' like the king of beasts or any earthly prince, revelling in the spring sunshine – a predestined victim of fortune's malice,

For evere the latter ende of joye is wo.

His tragic doom is already prepared for him in the shape of the fox, an agent of destiny, yet a traitor and murderer in his own right, lying hidden 'in a bed of wortes'. Chaucer, for all his digressions and asides, keeps in his mind's eye a clear picture of the farmyard on this bright May morning,[1] the cheerfulness of which throws into relief the dismal sequel:

Faire in the soond, to bathe hire myrily,
Lith Pertelote, and alle hire sustres by,
Agayn the sonne, and Chauntecleer so free
Soong murier than the mermayde in the see;
For Phisiologus seith sikerly
How that they syngen wel and myrily.

[1] Chaucer's way of reckoning the fatal date from 'the month in which the world bigan, / That highte March, whan God first maked man' naturally puzzles modern readers, who may be tempted to find hidden meanings. But Chaucer is simply counting from the beginning of the mediaeval calendar, in which March was the first month.

And so bifel that, as he caste his ye
Among the wortes on a boterflye,
He was war of this fox, that lay ful lowe.
Nothyng ne liste hym thanne for to crowe,
But cride anon, 'Cok! cok!' and up he sterte
As man that was affrayed in his herte.

The excitement of this moment, which we are made to share, adds to the effectiveness of the fox's speech, with its caressing and protesting tone:

'Gentil sire, allas! wher wol ye gon?
Be ye affrayed of me that am youre freend?
Now, certes, I were worse than a feend,
If I to yow wolde harm or vileynye!'

Irony and sanctimoniousness, too, are employed to make the fox a thoroughly enjoyable villain, with a touch of Richard III about him:

'My lord youre fader – God his soule blesse! –
And eek youre mooder, of hire gentillesse,
Han in myn hous ybeen to my greet ese . . .'

We see through his flattery (with Chaucer's help, of course), and are well aware why he wants Chauntecleer to shut both his eyes.[1] Expectation is heightened as the fatal moment is prolonged:

[1] The fox's persuasion to shut them is a prominent part of the story in the *Roman* and other earlier versions, in which the cock first feels some suspicion and crows with one eye shut. Chaucer, in whose time the story must have been very well known, perhaps felt that to repeat all this would be to labour the point, and therefore concentrated on the other aspect of the fox's flattery, his praise of Chauntecleer's father for his wisdom.

This Chauntecleer his wynges gan to bete,
As man that koude his traysoun nat espie,
So was he ravysshed with his flaterie.
Allas! ye lordes, many a fals flatour
Is in youre courtes . . . [*etc.*]

This Chauntecleer stood hye upon his toos,
Strecchynge his nekke, and heeld his eyen cloos,
And gan to crowe loude for the nones.
And daun Russell the fox stirte up atones,
And by the gargat hente Chauntecleer,
And on his bak toward the wode hym beer,
For yet ne was ther no man that hym sewed.

The climax of the story is reached: Chauntecleer is taken. It seems that now the tale must go on to its end. But Chaucer's line 'For yet ne was ther no man that hym sewed', while in one respect it makes the fox's success look secure by giving him a long start, in another respect holds the action suspended; so that, before the action resumes, there is time for one final burst of mock-heroics. Chaucer is too fertile an artist to allow his mock-heroics to grow repetitive and tiresome. Fresh ideas come crowding to his fancy. Having, I imagine, first thought of celebrating the rhetorician who so memorably chided the Friday on which Richard I received his death-wound, he likewise assigns Chauntecleer's disaster to a Friday, and then (by the same power of brilliant comic association that he has already shown in Pertelote's speech on choler) he indignantly apostrophizes Venus, in whose service Chauntecleer has been so devoted ('He fethered Pertelote twenty tyme, / And trad hire eke as ofte, er it was pryme'):

> Why woldestow suffre hym on thy day to dye?

The gods, it seems, are as involved in Chauntecleer's destiny as they are in the fates of Palamon and Arcite. Similarly, the lamentations of the hens, which are the signal of the farmyard disaster and bring the widow back into the story at last, suggest to Chaucer such classical disasters of history as the destruction of Troy, of Carthage, and of Rome.

There is no need to praise yet again the chase after the fox. Like the comic battle which ends *The Reeve's Tale*, it rushes along and carries the reader with it. Ducks, geese and bees are added to the other farmyard creatures in order that the most complete confusion may reign, and the fox is pursued with every imaginable outcry and uproar, both vocal and instrumental, not only by 'this sely wydwe and eek hir doghtres two' but also by 'many another man'. After so much of inaction and quiet dialogue in the earlier part of the story, the introduction of this tumultuous crowd is most exciting. It also throws into contrast the crucial dialogue which follows, in readiness for which Chaucer calms us down with

> Now, goode men, I prey yow herkneth alle.
> Lo, how Fortune turneth sodeynly
> The hope and pryde eek of hir enemy!

We are back to *The Monk's Tale* and to burlesque moralizing, for now begins the fox's tragedy – of not eating the cock. He too, no less than Chauntecleer, is overweening. The chance of insulting his outdistanced pursuers ('ye proude cherles alle') is more than he can resist, but he is denied even that satisfaction, for as soon as he opens his mouth to agree to Chauntecleer's suggestion, his proud boast becomes untrue and his jaws empty:

The fox answerde, 'In feith, it shal be don.'
And as he spak that word, al sodeynly
This cok brak from his mouth delyverly,
And heighe upon a tree he fleigh anon.

Chauntecleer has shown himself nimble both in body and in wit, and we applaud his escape. The remaining speeches rather state the story's lesson than continue the story itself – both Chauntecleer and the fox draw the appropriate general conclusions from their particular experience – though Daun Russell's apology is as ironical as his earlier blandishments:

'Com doun, and I shal telle yow what I mente;
I shal seye sooth to yow, God help me so!'

The concluding remarks repeat the moral lesson:

Lo, swich it is for to be recchelees
And necligent, and truste on flaterye.
But ye that holden this tale a folye,
As of a fox, or of a cok and hen,
Taketh the moralite, goode men.
For seinte Paul seith that al that writen is,
To oure doctrine it is ywrite, ywis;
Taketh the fruyt, and lat the chaf be stille.
Now, goode God, if that it be thy wille,
As seith my lord, so make us alle goode men,
And brynge us to his heighe blisse! Amen.

These lines do not mean that there is a subtler 'moralite' underlying the evident one, but that the evident one is worth marking, and is the 'fruyt' of the story. The 'chaf' is the story itself and the comicalities with which it has been garnished in the telling: a statement of the most winning and graceful modesty, for Chaucer has put all his mature art and his mature personality into *The Nun's Priest's Tale.*[1]

1 The prayer is Chaucer's usual way of ending a story, and has no special reference to 'the moralite' nor seemingly to the Nun's Priest (though nobody has satisfactorily explained the curious phrase 'As seith my lord'). The Host's jolly and appreciative remarks in the *Epilogue* direct us back to the merriment of the tale: 'This was a murie tale of Chauntecleer.'

V *Chaucer's Tale of Sir Thopas*
The Cook's Tale
The Canon's Yeoman's Tale

All three of these tales are, it is assumed, Chaucer's own inventions; in them, he departs from his usual practice of improving somebody else's story. They are treated together in this short chapter, since the two fragmentary tales told by the Cook and by Chaucer are unsuited by their brevity to a long discussion, and since (in my opinion at least) the Canon's Yeoman's story is not rich enough in comedy to deserve a chapter to itself.

Chaucer's own *Tale of Sir Thopas*, like that of the Monk and unlike those of the Cook and the Squire, breaks off not by apparent accident but by evident design. The Monk's series of tragedies is interrupted for the tediousness of its unrelieved melancholy; Chaucer's jigging romance is interrupted for its absolute tediousness. The Host, who has smiled benignly on Chaucer's timid undertaking of 'a rym I lerned longe agoon' –

> 'Ye, that is good', quod he; 'now shul we heere
> Som deyntee thyng, me thynketh by his cheere' –

frowns upon it as its 'second fit' begins, and rates Chaucer for his 'verray lewednesse' and 'drasty speche'.

The simple comedy of the Host's change of mood,

and the complex comedy of Chaucer's incompetence, are the things which chiefly please us today. The tale itself is not, I think, capable of giving much pleasure, though we enjoy its bathos ('He hadde a semely nose') and its naïveté (as when Sir Thopas announces, with no more concern than if it were a social engagement, his appointment to fight 'with a geaunt with hevedes three'). It has not the independent, self-contained interest of that other piece of literary humour, *The Nun's Priest's Tale*. This is partly because, whereas nobody but the student of mediaeval literature now reads those romances of which *Sir Thopas* is a derisive amalgam, everyone can still appreciate that comic disproportion which is the essence of the mock-heroic. A more important reason is that the interest of *The Nun's Priest's Tale* is not confined to its literary humour. The tale of Chauntecleer, full of fancy though it is, is also full of those 'just representations of general nature' which alone, according to Johnson, 'can please many and please long'. The characteristic dialogues, the varied moods, the felicitous expression, the wise and witty commentary, are all merits which a straightforward burlesque like *Sir Thopas* cannot by its very nature possess, since (to borrow another compendious phrase of Johnson's) 'probability is violated, life is misrepresented, and language is depraved' – as they are of course meant to be.

As a 'Canterbury Tale', the prime offence of *Sir Thopas* is that it has no narrative interest. It has a *story*, but that is by no means the same thing. The story, instead of being ingeniously prolonged (again like that of *The Nun's Priest's Tale*), is unbearably diffuse: there is but a half-pennyworth of sack to an intolerable deal of bread. The Host puts an end to the recital in the middle of a stanza, too impatient to care what happened 'on a day'. And so the tale remains half-told, not because Chaucer the writer (as distinct from the incompetent reciter) could not finish it, but because anybody could finish it all too easily. What elf-queen could resist the beauty of Sir Thopas? What giant, however many heads he had, could withstand his invincible might?

The Cook's Tale, on the contrary, has puzzled everyone to foresee its continuation. Indeed, this spirited fragment ends before a story has begun, although Chaucer has given us a situation – the idle apprentice, dismissed by his master, taking up residence with his thievish companion and the companion's prostitute wife – from which a story might follow. Nor has the tale been given any setting more particular than London, for the apprentice has left his master's shop, presumably never to return, when the fragment ends. The London setting of the tale follows very naturally from the Cook's prologue, in which, tickled by the Reeve's story ('For joye him thoughte he clawed him on the bak'), he undertakes to tell 'a lytel jape that fil in oure citee'. The cheerful rudeness that passes between him and the Host, another Londoner, who either knows the Cook's shop already or pretends to deduce its character from that of its owner, also brings the life of the city before us ('For in thy shoppe is many a flye loos'), and further details are added when the apprentice's pastimes are described. He sings and dances at weddings, plays at dice on street-corners, leaps out of the shop to see public processions pass by, and – in consequence of his disorderly enjoyments – is himself sometimes made a public spectacle, being led to prison with minstrels drawing attention to his disgrace. But the chief usefulness of these pastimes is to show us Perkyn Revelour in action. Perkyn, whose surname has been given him by his acquaintance, is portrayed in three vivid lines of bouncing alliteration:

> Gaillard he was as goldfynch in the shawe,
> Broun as a berye, a propre short felawe,
> With lokkes blake, ykembd ful fetisly.

He would have cut a striking figure in the *General Prologue*, and the commentary –

> For sikerly a prentys revelour
> That haunteth dys, riot, or paramour,
> His maister shal it in his shoppe abye,
> Al have he no part of the mynstralcye.
> For thefte and riot, they been convertible,
> Al konne he pleye on gyterne or ribible.
> Revel and trouthe, as in a lowe degree,
> They been ful wrothe al day, as men may see –

likewise recalls Chaucer's reflections on the various pilgrims' characters and behaviour. One is tempted to wonder whether, in *The Cook's Tale*, Chaucer has written a description before getting a story to attach it to. Yet to do this would be quite contrary to his method in *The Miller's Tale* and the other *fabliaux*, where the characters are fitted to (though not limited by) their parts in an already existing story.

The Canon's Yeoman's Tale, though it is complete, and though it contains some touches that no admirer of

Chaucer could spare, is like the two fragments in its comparative lack of interest as a story.

The prologue to this tale raises our expectations, for it contains as much poetry of action and of character as any of Chaucer's best links. The hasty approach of the Canon, and his hastier flight, are imaginatively conceived and are presented in apt and vivid detail, while the dialogue between the Host and the Canon's Yeoman is richly expressive, full of the tricks of everyday speech ('Telle me *that* . . .'), and full of character ('I am nat wont in no mirour to prie'). And the earlier part of the tale itself, the Yeoman's monologue after the vanishing of his master, may best be considered as a continuation of the prologue: a regretful, lively and informative piece of retrospection like the Wife of Bath's:

> Ther I was wont to be right fressh and gay
> Of clothyng and of oother good array,
> Now may I were an hose upon myn heed;
> And wher my colour was bothe fressh and reed,
> Now is it wan and of a leden hewe . . .

The general reflections, too, have much trenchant humour; the ironical invitation to the difficult study of alchemy, for example:

> Whoso that listeth outen his folie,
> Lat hym come forth and lerne multiplie;
> And every man that oght hath in his cofre,
> Lat hym appiere, and wexe a philosophre.
> Ascaunce that craft is so light to leere?
> Nay, nay, God woot, al be he monk or frere,
> Preest or chanoun, or any oother wyght,
> Though he sitte at his book bothe day and nyght

In lernyng of this elvysshe nyce loore,
Al is in veyn, and parde! muchel moore.
To lerne a lewed man this subtiltee –
Fy! spek nat therof, for it wol nat bee;
And konne he letterure, or konne he noon,
As in effect, he shal fynde it al oon.
For bothe two, by my savacioun,
Concluden in multiplicacioun
Ylike wel, whan they han al ydo;
This is to seyn, they faillen bothe two.

The jargon of alchemy, as contrasted with these reflections on the impossibility of turning base metals into gold, is somewhat tedious, like the jargon in Ben Jonson's *Alchemist*, the apothecary's jargon in John Heywood's *Four PP*, and indeed all jargon, the comic power of which is limited because the writer's own distinctive sense of humour has no means of showing through it. It resembles in its limitations the tags of mediaeval romance which Chaucer uses in *Sir Thopas*. What we remember from the Canon's Yeoman's monologue is the part where he discusses the enthusiasm – a very madness – of those who sincerely practise alchemy:

for nadde they but a sheete,
Which that they myghte wrappe hem inne a-nyght,
And a brat to walken inne by daylyght,
They wolde hem selle and spenden on this craft.
They kan nat stynte til no thyng be laft.
And everemoore, where that evere they goon,
Men may hem knowe by smel of brymstoon.
For al the world they stynken as a goot;
Hir savour is so rammyssh and so hoot
That though a man from hem a mile be,

The savour wole infecte hym, trusteth me.
And thus by smel, and by threedbare array,
If that men liste, this folk they knowe may.

Best of all, since action and dialogue here combine, is the account of a failed experiment in alchemy.

The pot tobreketh, and farewel, al is go!

The verse depicts the explosion; and the consequences, the atmosphere of brimstone fumes and disappointed selfishness, can be both comically and earnestly likened to that of hell:

Though that the feend noght in oure sighte hym
  shewe,
I trowe he with us be, that ilke shrewe!
In helle, where that he lord is and sire,
Nis ther moore wo, ne moore rancour ne ire.
Whan that oure pot is broke, as I have sayd,
Every man chit, and halt hym yvele apayd.

Various complaints are vigorously expressed by the dupes, a plausible explanation is put forward by the Canon, and a pathetic and ridiculous voice is heard hoping for better luck next time:

'Pardee', quod oon, 'somwhat of oure metal
Yet is ther heere, though that we han nat al.
Although this thyng myshapped have as now,
Another tyme it may be well ynow.
Us moste putte oure good in aventure.
A marchant, pardee, may nat ay endure,
Trusteth me wel, in his prosperitee.
Somtyme his good is drowned in the see,
And somtyme comth it sauf unto the londe.'

This incident is the climax of the monologue, and Chaucer wisely refrains from continuing after it.

With the 'second part' of the tale, the Canon's Yeoman's own experience ends, and his story proper begins. A canon, pretending to a knowledge of alchemy, dupes a priest by performing experiments in his presence; with great craftiness, and in a variety of ways, he fakes successful results; finally he sells the supposed secret to the priest for forty pounds, and absconds. Chaucer's description of the rogue's tricks is clear and detailed, and has some technical and historical interest comparable with that of Elizabethan coney-catching exposures. At its best moments, it has permanent human interest too, for the rogue's self-praise is rich in conscious irony –

> 'Ye', quod the chanoun soon,
> 'Though poure I be, crafty thou shalt me fynde.
> I warne thee, yet is ther moore bihynde' –

and his whole dialogue with the priest is expressive of their characters.

Nevertheless, as a comic story *The Canon's Yeoman's Tale* is undeveloped and unrelieved, especially if we contrast it with *The Alchemist*. Where Jonson's play has assorted characters, diverse motives, compound knavery, bustling action and perpetual surprise, Chaucer's tale has only two characters (if we exclude the priest's servant, who exists merely to fetch and carry), and he shows us them only in simple contrast as knave and fool. He does not make us *see* either of them, as he makes us see even so minor a character as the carpenter's servant in *The Miller's Tale*.

The relationship between the knave and the fool, moreover, has no prospect of development, and hence there is no suspense and no prospect of surprise. The knave is an absolute knave, and the fool an absolute fool:

> Noght wiste this preest with whom that he delte,
> Ne of his harm comynge he no thyng felte.

The knavery is premeditated from the start of the tale, and has less narrative interest than the sudden spontaneous opportunism of the clerks in *The Reeve's Tale*. It also has less moral interest either than the situation where the dupe overreaches his deceiver (as when John and Aleyn repay Symkyn for his theft of their corn) or than the situation where the dupe is wise in his own conceit (as is John the carpenter in *The Miller's Tale*).

Lastly, the story allows no digression; the only way in which Chaucer can relieve the narrative is by supplying a commentary. But the situation and the characterization are so elementary that the commentary itself can only be elementary and repetitive:

> Loo, how this theef koude his service beede!
>
> Now taak heede of this chanons cursednesse!
>
> And taaketh heede now of his cursed sleighte![1]

The tale told by the Canon's Yeoman, then, is inferior to Chaucer's best comic tales. Its vigorous context,

[1] At one point I think the punctuation of all editions that I have seen could be improved: at line 1236, the canon, who has just secretly introduced a bit of real silver, tells the priest

> 'Loke what ther is, put in thyn hand and grope.
> Thow fynde shalt ther silver, as I hope.'

The next two lines are surely commentary, though always printed as part of the speech:

> What devel of helle sholde it elles be?
> Shaving of silver silver is, pardee!

indeed, rather injures it than improves it. We may here contrast it with the prologue and tale of the Wife of Bath. Her tale gains in effectiveness because it has nothing directly to do with her personal experiences as recounted in her prologue, while at the same time its theme aptly reflects her belief that wives should rule their husbands. Now *The Canon's Yeoman's Tale* largely duplicates its own prologue, with this difference, that it loses the zest that personal reminiscence can give:

> This chanon was my lord, ye wolden weene?
> Sire hoost, in feith, and by the hevenes queene,
> It was another chanoun, and nat hee,
> That kan an hundred foold moore subtiltee.

It is as though the Wife of Bath had followed up her fivefold marriage-history by telling how some other wife had got the better of some other husband.

VI *The Friar's Tale*

The Friar's Tale and *The Summoner's Tale*, with their prologues, form a complete group; and in them, more than in any other tale, the story is connected with its teller's satirical purpose. This does not mean that throughout both tales we are aware of the tellers' personalities. For, as always, the tale soon begins to tell, or rather act, itself; and although we are at times reminded of the narrator's personal rancour, either by Chaucer's direct mention of him (' "This false theef, this somonour", quod the Frere . . .'; ' "So thryve I", quod this Somonour, "so I shal!" ') or by a satiric comment of his own, this rancour is never allowed to get in the way of the story-telling, any more than the Miller's drunkenness is allowed to prevent his telling a wonderfully coherent story. In fact, with one difference, Chaucer handles their malice as he has handled the Reeve's, whose prologue states his motives and whose closing lines of narrative remind us of them. The difference is that in both *The Friar's Tale* and *The Summoner's Tale* Chaucer has added a further reminder of the teller's malice by making his opponent object to the tale while it is being told. As usual, Chaucer varies his method. In *The Friar's Tale* it is the teller who takes the offensive, and, while describing his fictitious summoner, suddenly points to the pilgrim Summoner:

> 'For thogh this Somonour wood were as an hare,
> To telle his harlotrye I wol nat spare;

For we been out of his correccioun.
They han of us no jurisdiccioun,
Ne nevere shullen, terme of alle hir lyves.'
'Peter! so been the wommen of the styves',
Quod the Somonour, 'yput out of oure cure!' . . .

The intentional ambiguities of the first three lines ('this Somonour' is the pilgrim, to whom 'his correccioun' also refers, while 'his harlotrye' is the roguery of the fictitious summoner) help the Friar to demonstrate that the vices of the fictitious summoner are those of summoners in general and of the pilgrim Summoner in particular. In *The Summoner's Tale* it is the victim, not the aggressor, who brings out the professional and personal hostility in the tale. When the fictitious friar erases his benefactors' names from his list as soon as he is out of their sight, the pilgrim Friar's protest –

'Nay, ther thou lixt, thou Somonour!' quod the Frere –

shows that the thrust has really gone home; the Friar displays his guilt just as Claudius displays his when the poison is poured into the ear of the sleeping player king.

What these interruptions have in common is that they come near the beginnings of the two tales, because in this position they will only interrupt the characterization, not the plot. Once the plot is begun, further commentary could add nothing to its satire – for it is essentially satirical – and would only obscure its outline.

The Friar's Tale is essentially satirical, as everyone agrees, and this, coupled with its narrator's malicious purpose, has overshadowed for many readers its comic virtues. It is obvious that the Friar's remark to the Wife of Bath –

'Ye han seyd muche thyng right wel, I seye;
But, dame, heere as we ryde by the weye,
Us nedeth nat to speken but of game . . .'

is merely a diplomatic preparation for his earnest enough attack, in which he makes the other pilgrims his accomplices:

'But if it lyke to this compaignye,
I wol yow of a somonour telle a game.'

Yet it should be just as obvious that his tale is essentially a comedy of character and situation, with its conceited summoner offering the fiend advice, and, like Symkyn in *The Reeve's Tale*, justly becoming the victim of his own cunning and complacency. Like *The Reeve's Tale*, *The Merchant's Tale* and *The Summoner's Tale*, it is a farce exhibiting poetic justice.

Like them, accordingly, it opens with a critical account of the chief character. These openings may be contrasted with those of *The Miller's Tale* and *The Shipman's Tale* (in which rewards and punishments are casual or unimportant), where the carpenter and the merchant are rapidly summed up and dismissed, and where the more elaborately-described characters (Nicholas, Alison, Absolon) are treated with the lightest irony.

The satirical portrait of the summoner introduces the tale proper, but it is itself introduced by another portrait, that of his employer the archdeacon,

That boldely dide execucioun
In punysshynge of fornicacioun,
Of wicchecraft, and eek of bawderye,
Of diffamacioun, and avowtrye,

Of chirche reves, and of testamentz,
Of contractes and of lakke of sacramentz,
Of usure, and of symonye also . . .

By thus beginning with the archdeacon, Chaucer gives the summoner a realistic and substantial background, like the miller's mill in *The Reeve's Tale*. He also bestows a side-stroke on the whole system of raising ecclesiastical revenue from the profitable sins of the wicked; and he thereby approaches the summoner's moral character through that of his employer. Though the system from which summoners get their living is a rotten one, I think Chaucer draws a distinction between the archdeacon's fanatical zeal in punishing sinners according to the law of the ecclesiastical courts (I see him as a kind of Angelo), and the summoner's basely calculating and self-interested energy ('He koude spare of lecchours oon or two,/ To techen hym to foure and twenty mo'). The summoner does his unpleasant office as a mere matter of business. He is a hireling, a tool, but a crafty one:

He hadde a somonour redy to his hond;
A slyer boye nas noon in Engelond.

His cunning consists not in performing his duty but in corrupting it; employing tools of his own, he

Hadde alwey bawdes redy to his hond
As any hauk to lure in Engelond,
That tolde hym al the secree that they knewe;
For hire acqueyntance was nat come of newe.
They weren his approwours prively.

(The official-sounding term shows up the most unofficial relationship.)

He took hymself a greet profit therby;
His maister knew nat alwey what he wan.
Withouten mandement a lewed man
He koude somne, on peyne of Cristes curs,
And they were gladde for to fille his purs,
And make hym grete feestes atte nale.
And right as Judas hadde purses smale,
And was a theef, right swich a theef was he;
His maister hadde but half his duetee.
He was, if I shal yeven hym his laude,
A theef, and eek a somnour, and a baude.

There is a delicate balance, in itself amusing, between the justified moral disgust for this Judas of a summoner and the malicious relish of his epigrammatic dismissal ('A theef, and eek a somnour, and a baude'), where 'somnour' is by definition a term of abuse; the Friar has already made the point in his prologue –

'Pardee, ye may wel knowe by the name
That of a somonour may no good be sayd' –

and will make it again:

He dorste nat, for verray filthe and shame,
Seye that he was a somonour, for the name.

Chaucer is still very conscious of the narrator, and it is typical of the Friar that, not content to let his epigram comprehend the summoner's sins (which it perfectly does), he plunges straight back into illustrative detail with satirical delight:

He hadde eek wenches at his retenue,
That, whether that sir Robert or sir Huwe,

Or Jakke, or Rauf, or whoso that it were
That lay by hem, they tolde it in his ere.
Thus was the wenche and he of oon assent;
And he wolde fecche a feyned mandement,
And somne hem to chapitre bothe two,
And pile the man, and lete the wenche go.
Thanne wolde he seye, 'Freend, I shal for thy sake
Do striken hire out of oure lettres blake;
Thee thar namoore as in this cas travaille.
I am thy freend, ther I thee may availle.'

Though this adds nothing to the charge, it adds a good deal to the portrait; the summoner's hypocrisy is made vivid by his unctuous speech, and his unsavoury familiarity with the prostitutes is made concrete by the phrase 'they tolde it in his ere'. We are thus led to dislike the summoner in person, as well as on principle.

Having given him personal reality, Chaucer can now set him, and the story, in action.

And so bifel that ones on a day
This somnour, evere waityng on his pray,
Rood for to somne an old wydwe, a ribibe,
Feynynge a cause, for he wolde brybe.
And happed that he saugh bifore hym ryde
A gay yeman, under a forest syde.
A bowe he bar, and arwes brighte and kene;
He hadde upon a courtepy of grene,
An hat upon his heed with frenges blake.
'Sire', quod this somnour, 'hayl, and wel atake!'

This is a good example of Chaucer's economy in storytelling. The brief account of the summoner's purpose is useful. It not only starts him convincingly on his way, but also lurks in our memory during all his dealings with the fiend, letting us expect that he will in some manner overreach himself when he gets to the widow's house, though the story moves so fast that we never foresee exactly how he will do it, even when we reach the incident of the cursing carter. The setting of the encounter, 'under a forest syde', is well chosen: the lonely place encourages the conversation and companionship between the summoner and the fiend, essential to the irony of situation and to the satire. It also, like the sinister black fringes on the supposed yeoman's hat, prepares us to believe Chaucer when he reveals that the stranger has just sprung up from hell.[1] Meanwhile we see him through the eyes of the summoner (his contemptuous opinion of the widow, 'a ribibe', has opened his consciousness to us), whose greeting, 'Hayl, and wel atake!', launches the dramatic irony of the tale, for this overtaking turns out far from luckily for the summoner; it is not only the summoner, but the fiend too, who is 'evere waityng on his pray'.

The following conversation improves the dramatic irony of the situation and the satiric force of the tale. The stranger, greeting the summoner as a 'good felawe' (which in Chaucer's time had the secondary meaning 'rascal'),[2] asks 'Wiltow fer to-day?'; and the summoner replies 'Nay', though he will later be told 'Thou shalt with me to helle yet to-nyght'. The summoner then naturally goes on to state his business near by. He

[1] In the preceding tale, that of the Wife of Bath, the knight's encounter with the dancing fairies, who immediately vanish, is likewise 'under a forest syde' (990).

[2] See *General Prologue*, 395, and Robinson's note; 649-651, 653. The last two illustrations come from the account of the Summoner, which Chaucer undoubtedly had in mind while writing *The Friar's Tale*.

lyingly declares that he is collecting a rent for his lord, though he is really extorting a bribe for himself, and he permits the inference that he is a bailiff, because (as the Friar stresses) he is ashamed of his real dirty trade. In reply the stranger claims brotherhood because he also is a bailiff. This, of course, turns out to be equally a lie, and equally an apt euphemism, so that the striking up of brotherhood between a fiend and a summoner is a sharp satirical thrust against the latter.

Chaucer encourages us to guess the stranger's real identity before the stranger reveals it to the summoner. 'I am unknowen as in this contree', he cryptically remarks, and when pressed to say where he does live, he answers with sinister quietness that he dwells 'fer in the north contree', and promises to direct his new brother thither before they part (but the summoner finds his own way there all too easily). The summoner, in addition to his graver faults, is a talkative busybody, 'evere enqueryng upon every thyng', and it is his questions that produce these evasive and sinister replies. When he asks the stranger to teach him 'som subtiltee', some tricks of the bailiff's trade, he is told a fact which is crucial to the story:

> 'For sothe, I take al that men wol me yive.'

This most important idea is skilfully worked into the dialogue, which then naturally and consequently continues with the summoner's boast that he too snaps up anything he can get, that his conscience is calloused and his soul unshriven. He is in such a promising state of obduracy that when he now impertinently presses the stranger for his name, the fiend can show his hand:

'Brother,' quod he, 'wiltow that I thee telle?
I am a feend; my dwellyng is in helle,
And heere I ryde aboute my purchasyng,
To wite wher men wol yeve me any thyng.
My purchas is th'effect of al my rente.
Looke how thou rydest for the same entente,
To wynne good, thou rekkest nevere how;
Right so fare I, for ryde wolde I now
Unto the worldes ende for a preye.'

This last remark is designed to conceal from the summoner, who is at the fiend's elbow, his own danger. And the summoner suspects nothing; after a momentary shock at meeting a devil, he is quite himself again:

'A!' quod this somonour, '*benedicite*! what sey ye?
I wende ye were a yeman trewely.
Ye han a mannes shap as wel as I.
Han ye a figure thanne determinat
In helle, ther ye been in youre estat?'

He is surprised that the devil is not wearing tail and horns but a human form like his own (a reminder to us that the summoner himself has a man's body and a devil's soul), but instead of showing a moral horror of the devil's company, he merely shows a trivial and impertinent curiosity as to the natural form of devils in hell.

This curiosity, which Chaucer has already established as part of the summoner's character, aptly introduces the fiend's long exposition of the nature and extent of diabolical powers in God's universe. Chaucer obviously enjoys this theological excursion, illustrated from scripture and legend, as he enjoys the discourses on dreams and on predestination in *The Nun's Priest's Tale*, but it is far from being a self-indulgent digression on his part. The fiend insists that without God's permission the devils have no power either to tempt or harm; that sometimes God allows them to tempt a good man and thereby exercise his virtue; and that sometimes they are

> 'Goddes instrumentz,
> And meenes to doon his comandementz,
> Whan that hym list, upon his creatures,
> In divers art and in diverse figures.'

It is clear enough that the summoner has been divinely marked out for the devil's attentions. Consequently we feel no misgivings about siding with the fiend against him, for in so doing we can be on God's side and the devil's at once.

And certainly we must prefer the urbane, witty, ironical fiend to the brutal, vulgar, conceited summoner. The characters of both are kept before us; Chaucer, for all his interest in the theology, never loses sight of context and speaker ('I do no fors of youre dyvynytee'), and the fiend's conclusion is admirable:

> 'But o thing warne I thee, I wol nat jape –
> Thou wolt algates wite how we been shape;
> Thou shalt herafterward, my brother deere,
> Come there thee nedeth nat of me to leere.
> For thou shalt, by thyn owene experience,
> Konne in a chayer rede of this sentence
> Bet than Virgile, while he was on lyve,
> Or Dant also. Now lat us ryde blyve,
> For I wole holde compaignye with thee
> Til it be so that thou forsake me.'

The academic contrast between 'experience' and 'authority' as sources of knowledge; the hit at the summoner's frivolous scholastic curiosity which, when satisfied, will qualify him for a professorial chair; the literary joke about Virgil, who described the underworld twice, his ghost being Dante's well-informed guide in hell – all these mark the fiend's inward triumph, in which we join, over the summoner's stupidity. His closing remark, implying for us that he will stick to the summoner as long as the summoner sticks to the devil's principles, is taken literally by his companion –

> 'Nay', quod this somonour, 'that shal nat bityde!' –

who boastfully makes a virtue of his constancy to the fiend. This knits up the satirical theme of brotherhood.

The sworn brothers ride on, and encounter a cart stuck in the road. The place is important, for it is

> right at the entryng of the townes ende,
> To which this somonour shoop hym for to wende.

This recalls the summoner's object, and lets us know that this affair of the cart will be merely an episode, the story's climax being reserved for the widow's house. But this is an important episode, as well as being the first piece of physical action since the tale began, and Chaucer makes it vivid. His versification, as usual, is dramatic, presenting first the abrupt halt of the cart, and then the impassioned flow and deliberate final emphasis of the carter's language:

> And right at the entryng of the townes ende,
> To which this somonour shoop hym for to wende,
> They saugh a cart that charged was with hey,
> Which that a cartere droof forth in his wey.

Deep was the wey, for which the carte stood.
The cartere smoot, and cryde as he were wood,
'Hayt, Brok! hayt, Scot! what spare ye for the stones?
The feend', quod he, 'yow fecche, body and bones,
As ferforthly as evere were ye foled,
So muche wo as I have with yow tholed!
The devel have al, bothe hors and cart and hey!'

All Chaucer's penetration and humanity appear in this spirited sketch of the carter who first curses his beasts and then blesses them, and who is typical of human inconsistency. For all his momentary wrath, the carter is evidently fond of his horses ('That was wel twight, myn owene lyard boy'), and of course God will share Chaucer's view of the matter, and will not allow the devil to take the cursing carter at his word – if, indeed, this were so unscrupulous a devil as to wish to do so. Only the summoner, who has no sense of true justice, thinks of exploiting the letter of the law, and he is perfectly odious in his sly, exultant and officious advice to the fiend to look sharp:

This somonour seyde, 'Heere shal we have a pley.'
And neere the feend he drough, as noght ne were,
Ful prively, and rowned in his ere:
'Herkne, my brother, herkne, by thy feith!
Herestow nat how that the cartere seith?
Hent it anon, for he hath yeve it thee,
Bothe hey and cart, and eek his caples thre.'
'Nay', quod the devel, 'God woot, never a deel!
It is nat his entente, trust me weel.'

The fiend, whose justice exceeds the summoner's, allows that, in cursing, sincerity is what matters. He repeats the point ('The carl spak oo thing, but he thoghte another'), so that we remember it at the climax of the tale.

That we are reaching this climax is now made plain:

Whan that they coomen somwhat out of towne,
This somonour to his brother gan to rowne:
'Brother', quod he, 'heere woneth an old rebekke,
That hadde almoost as lief to lese hire nekke
As for to yeve a peny of hir good.
I wole han twelf pens, though that she be wood,
Or I wol sompne hire unto oure office;
And yet, God woot, of hire knowe I no vice.
But for thou kanst nat, as in this contree,
Wynne thy cost, taak heer ensample of me.'

We know already that the summoner has no charge against the widow, and his remarks here, besides confirming the fact, show his ruthlessness and his vanity, which have already been shown in his rejected advice to seize the cart and horses. Injured vanity perhaps dictates his insulting offer to teach the fiend his own business:

'But for thou kanst nat, as in this contree,
Wynne thy cost, taak heer ensample of me.'

This boast is the height of dramatic irony, for the fiend knows well enough what he is about, and has been playing for the summoner's soul all along. Of his own danger the summoner has no conception; yet the fiend has shown his hand so clearly that we do not feel him to be taking unfair advantage of his victim. 'Taak heer ensample of me' thus keeps us in mind of him, watching and waiting, throughout the following forty lines of dialogue in which he takes no part.

This somonour clappeth at the wydwes gate.
'Com out', quod he, 'thou olde virytrate!
I trowe thou hast som frere or preest with thee.'[1]

He begins to abuse her before she has time to answer his knock, and his bullying arrogance is thrown into relief by her humility;

'God save you, sire, what is youre sweete wille?'

'Sweete' is highly inappropriate, and the blessing is charged with dramatic irony; but the irony is of course the situation's, not the widow's, and it is increased when the summoner replies to her blessing with a summons to the ecclesiastical court 'up peyne of cursyng' (he is himself to be cursed, most effectively, before the end of the story). All his chief vices now pass before us in rapid review: his unpleasantly brisk business-like manner in agreeing to deputize for the widow, his cunning in affecting to calculate a sum he has already decided upon, his fraudulence in pretending that the profit is not his own, and, above all, his greedy brutal haste:

'Yis', quod this somonour, 'pay anon, lat se,
Twelf pens to me, and I wol thee acquite.
I shal no profit han therby but lite.
My maister hath the profit, and nat I.
Com of, and lat me ryden hastily;
Yif me twelf pens, I may no lenger tarye.'

1 The summoner's slur on the clergy shows his contempt for the religion he nominally serves. The point is, I think, Chaucer's and not the Friar's (in whose mouth the reference to friars would be strangely self-conscious). But when, near the beginning of the tale, the prostitutes betray the misconduct of 'sir Robert or sir Huwe', this may be the Friar's deliberate gird at the immoral life of parish priests. The friar in *The Summoner's Tale* several times speaks slightingly of priests.

The simple widow's pious and earnest protestations contrast sharply with his own random oaths, among which

> 'Nay thanne', quod he, 'the foule feend me fecche
> If I th'excuse, though thou shul be spilt!'

is prophetic of his fate. Chaucer here again reminds us of the fiend's continued presence, while he leaves us guessing how the fiend will capture the summoner, who has not yet damned himself, and who could not scrupulously be taken at his word if he did.

We are answered by the *dénouement*. The summoner, whose own boasts have committed him to extorting twelve pence from the widow, is balked by the fact that she has not got twelve pence to give him. He therefore falls back on bluster and on invention (his abrupt 'Pay me', besides showing a harsh and ugly mood, shows discomfiture and desperation too):

> 'Pay me', quod he, 'or by the sweete seinte Anne,
> As I wol bere awey thy newe panne,
> For dette which thou owest me of old.
> Whan that thou madest thyn housbonde cokewold,
> I payde at hoom for thy correccioun.'

And it is this mention of her pan that draws her curse upon him, because, being a concrete object, it naturally provokes the retort 'The devil take you and it!' Chaucer's thorough grasp of character precludes the simple ending of the analogues, in which an extortioner is suddenly met, and sincerely cursed, by one or more of his former victims.[1] Such spontaneous cursing is foreign to the old widow's character. She would never have cursed the summoner for his extortions, if he had not put it in her

[1] Examples are printed in *Sources and Analogues*, pp. 269-274.

mind by the combined effects of mentioning the pan, cursing himself if he showed mercy, and angering her with his lie that she once cuckolded her husband. Her curse is thus wholly, and justly, of his own making.

Though the summoner, rattled and embarrassed, is not cool enough to consider the seriousness of her curse, it is not lost upon his companion:

> '. . . Unto the devel blak and rough of hewe
> Yeve I thy body and my panne also!'
> And whan the devel herde hire cursen so
> Upon hire knees, he seyde in this manere,
> 'Now Mabely, myn owene mooder deere,
> Is this youre wyl in ernest that ye seye?'
> 'The devel', quod she, 'so fecche hym er he deye,
> And panne and al, but he wol hym repente!'
> 'Nay, olde stot, that is nat myn entente',
> Quod this somonour, 'for to repente me
> For any thyng that I have had of thee.
> I wolde I hadde thy smok and every clooth!'
> 'Now, brother', quod the devel, 'be nat wrooth;
> Thy body and this panne been myne by right.
> Thou shalt with me to helle yet to-nyght,
> Where thou shalt knowen of oure privetee
> Moore than a maister of dyvynytee.'
> And with that word this foule feend hym hente . . .

The devil is not 'blak and rough of hewe' as the widow imagines him, but smooth and courteous, and his respect for the widow (whom he addresses by the formal 'ye' and by name) shows up the abusive vulgarity of the summoner (to whom she is just an 'olde stot'). His courtesy extends even to the summoner, though it is now ironical in its reminder of their sworn brotherhood and of the summoner's ill-fated curiosity. Thus justice is done on the summoner, whose obdurate avarice and stupid conceit recoil upon himself: trying to rob the widow of her pan, he forfeits body and soul; trying to outdo the fiend, he is himself outdone. The devil's unemotional collection of both his prizes –

'Thy body and this panne been myne by right' –

puts the last ludicrous touch to the summoner's downfall.

That is the end of the summoner, and now the narrator makes an end of his story:

And with that word this foule feend hym hente;
Body and soule he with the devel wente
Where as that somonours han hir heritage.
And God, that maked after his ymage
Mankynde, save and gyde us, alle and some,
And leve thise somonours goode men bicome!

The observation about the natural place of summoners, and the special clause added to the prayer, throw us back suddenly to the tone of the prologue and opening of the tale ('A theef, and eek a somnour, and a baude'). This instantly recognizable note of malice shows how far the greater part of the tale is from being a direct expression of the Friar's personality. The point can be developed by contrasting his next remarks –

Lordynges, I koude han toold yow, quod this Frere,
Hadde I had leyser for this Somnour heere,
After the text of Crist, Poul, and John,
And of oure othere doctours many oon,
Swiche peynes that youre hertes myghte agryse,
Al be it so no tonge may it devyse,

Thogh that I myghte a thousand wynter telle
The peynes of thilke cursed hous of helle . . . –

with the fiend's account of his diabolical powers, in the tale. The latter, to say nothing of its self-contained irony and its aptitude to the speaker, is neat and systematic, and shows none of those loose connexions (' . . . of Crist, Poul, and John, / And of oure *othere* doctours') or large gestures ('Thogh that I myghte a thousand wynter telle') which are the vices of the Friar's style, and, as such, are burlesqued in the friar's harangue to Thomas in *The Summoner's Tale*.[1] In short, that the Friar is forgotten for most of the tale which he tells is one of that tale's many virtues.

[1] In the opening account of the summoner's character we again find this vice:

Certeyn he knew of briberyes mo
Than possible is to telle in yeres two.

VII *The Summoner's Tale*

The Summoner's retort to the Friar, announced in the Wife of Bath's prologue, has been announced a second time in that of the Friar:

> 'Nay', quod the Somonour, 'lat hym seye to me
> What so hym list; whan it comth to my lot,
> By God! I shal hym quiten every grot.'

Accordingly, at the end of *The Friar's Tale*, Chaucer wastes no time in saying how the pilgrims liked it, nor even in bringing in the Summoner with some such phrase as 'when the Friar had ended his story'. The quarrel simply *continues*:

> This Somonour in his styropes hye stood;
> Upon this Frere his herte was so wood
> That lyk an aspen leef he quook for ire.[1]

Impatient for battle, he anticipates his tale with an anecdote, taking up the Friar's remark about hell,

> Where as that somonours han hir heritage,

and refining on it: he consigns every friar not merely to hell but to its most disgusting region, 'the develes ers',

[1] This is like the middle of the later quarrel between the Cook and the Manciple:

> And with this speche the Cook wax wrooth and wraw,
> And on the Manciple he gan nodde faste
> For lakke of speche, and doun the hors hym caste,
> Where as he lay, til that men hym up took.

> That is his heritage of verray kynde.

This anecdote, besides keeping up the violent quarrel, looks forward to the unsavoury climax of the tale it introduces:

> Amydde his hand he leet the frere a fart.

When this climax is considered, the peculiar character of *The Summoner's Tale* becomes clear. Though almost as long as *The Miller's Tale*, and much longer than the Reeve's, the Shipman's, and its immediate predecessor and rival the Friar's, it has a very elementary plot. Most of its length is given over to a friar's begging visit to a sick man, who expresses his contempt by a worthless and insulting gift.

There exists a French *fabliau* in which a good priest, badgered on his death-bed by begging friars, contemptuously bequeaths them his bladder and tells them to keep their pepper in it. Chaucer may have known this *fabliau*, or some other like it, but whereas the main interest of *Li Dis de le Vescie a Prestre* lies in irony and anticipation, Chaucer's tale is chiefly concerned with characterization and surprise. 'The Summoner must tell a tale at the expense of a Friar; the character of the Friar must then be the important matter, not the plot, not the character of the sick man; and not irony, which, in any case, had just been exploited in *The Friar's Tale*.'[1]

One result of this difference in treatment is that the *fabliau* and Chaucer's story end differently. The substance of the *fabliau* is the contrast between the priest's intended bequest and the friars' great expectations, and so, when these expectations are dashed, the story very

[1] Walter Morris Hart, who has edited the *fabliau* in *Sources and Analogues*, pp. 277-286.

properly ends. In *The Summoner's Tale*, only twenty lines separate the sick man's proposal of a gift from the astonished friar's angry reception of it. The gift is a surprise to us, as well as to the friar. Therefore, to prevent an abrupt end, and to let us enjoy the friar's discomfiture in retrospect, Chaucer gives us the fantastic humour of the *coda*, in which a seemingly insoluble problem is solved:

> Who sholde make a demonstracion
> That every man sholde have yliche his part
> As of the soun or savour of a fart?

This last part of the tale is perhaps Chaucer's invention, for no known source or analogue exists. We shall see, later, how well he connects it with the body of the story. But first we must consider the portrait of the friar, which, dramatically speaking, is the Summoner's reason for telling the tale:

> I shal hym tellen which a greet honour
> It is to be a flaterynge lymytour.

The vices of the summoner in *The Friar's Tale* require, and receive, comparatively little space. He is a dishonest hireling whose cheats can be neatly and effectively summarized. The friar in *The Summoner's Tale*, on the other hand, gets his living not by deeds but by words, and must accordingly be shown practising his calculated rhetoric.

The Summoner's Tale opens in a rural setting, in which the friar goes about deluding the simple villagers (hence, when one of them deludes the friar, the effect is one of poetic justice). The friary, referred to but never seen, and the lord's manor-house with its sophisticated company, later complete the social picture. The opening lines pithily sum up the friar's function:

> Lordynges, ther is in Yorkshire, as I gesse,
> A merssshy contree called Holdernesse,
> In which ther wente a lymytour aboute,
> To preche, and eek to begge, it is no doute.

Preaching and begging are the same thing with friars. This is the Summoner paying back the Friar in his own coin ('A theef, and eek a somnour, and a baude'); but whereas the general satire on summoners is parcelled up before the close-knit ironical story of *The Friar's Tale* begins, the looser and slighter story of *The Summoner's Tale* can begin at once, the particular friar embodying the vices of all his kind.

> And so bifel that on a day this frere
> Hadde preched at a chirche in his manere.

The sermon, as reported, has neither text nor religious doctrine; as the friar later says, it is

> a sermon after my symple wit,
> Nat al after the text of hooly writ,

and its substance is, in the words of the *General Prologue*, that

> Men moote yeve silver to the povre freres,

for the upkeep of their friaries and for the rapid dispatch of trental masses for the dead: monasteries, he says, are rich enough already; and priests, singing only one trental mass in a day, he compares unfavourably with friars – who are ready to rush through all thirty, we presume. He thus reduces trental masses to a mere magic charm, and hurries his hearers into giving money for them by threatening that the dead will suffer until the magic charm has been gabbled out:

> 'Delivereth out', quod he, 'anon the soules!
> Ful hard it is with flesshhook or with oules
> To been yclawed, or to brenne or bake.
> Now spede yow hastily, for Cristes sake!'
> And whan this frere had seyd al his entente,
> With *qui cum patre* forth his wey he wente.

This final couplet, suggesting the friar's mechanical recitation of the formula as he briskly steps down from the pulpit to collect the money, leads on to his next move.

> Whan folk in chirche had yeve him what hem leste,
> He wente his wey, no lenger wolde he reste,
> With scrippe and tipped staf, ytukked hye –

and began on the houses, his next business appointment. Here his behaviour is just as indecent as in church.

> In every hous he gan to poure and prye,
> And beggeth mele and chese, or elles corn.

In short, he makes himself a nuisance, and people cannot refuse him once he has seen what they have got. While a second friar writes down the givers' names, a dramatic shift to direct speech sets before us the begging friar in all his unctuousness, flattering the women and listing desirable gifts. The third member of the begging party, 'a sturdy harlot', carries the spoils in a sack; evidently it needed a strong man to carry off these poor trifles, 'what yow lyst, we may nat cheese'. Worst of all, no sooner is the friar out of the house than he erases the givers' names, written down 'ascaunces that he wolde for hem preye'. This, a part of his ordinary cynical routine, suggests that all his sermon was equally a lie, and that friars discharge none of the religious duties that they undertake.

The outburst of the pilgrim Friar at this point is variously useful. Dramatic in itself, it also underlines the satire (the Friar winces like a galled jade), and moreover it marks off the beginning of the friar's approaching misfortune at Thomas's house. The narrative, after the interruption, resumes:

> So longe he wente, hous by hous, til he
> Cam til an hous ther he was wont to be
> Refresshed moore than in an hundred placis.
> Syk lay the goode man whos that the place is;
> Bedrede upon a couche lowe he lay.

This particular house is not only the last of a series, it is one where the friar usually enjoys special success. Therefore, this time, he will suffer conspicuous failure. And because this idea has just been suggested to us, we connect it with the bed-ridden householder, who is pointed out with the same kind of interest as the baby in *The Reeve's Tale* ('in cradel it lay'). The friar's entry, full of complacent reminiscence, further prepares us for his downfall:

> '*Deus hic*!' quod he, 'o Thomas, freend, good day!'
> Seyde this frere, curteisly and softe.
> 'Thomas', quod he, 'God yelde yow! ful ofte
> Have I upon this bench faren ful weel;
> Heere have I eten many a myrie meel.'
> And fro the bench he droof awey the cat,
> And leyde adoun his potente and his hat,
> And eek his scrippe, and sette hym softe adoun.

The 'business' here is truly dramatic. The friar's unfeeling treatment of the cat (for there seems to be plenty of room on the bench for his things as well as for himself), and his deliberate settling into the warm place it has just left, speak his whole character. And in the process, the setting is taking shape – the living-room of the house, the couch, the bench, the cat; later the wife will come in from the yard, and will talk of the boar in the sty; and while the friar pays his visit, the other friar and the servant have walked as far as the village inn, where all three intend to lodge that night.

From the sick man's greeting we learn that the friar has not visited him for more than a fortnight, and the friar, seemingly scenting dissatisfaction, begins to justify himself:

> 'God woot', quod he, 'laboured have I ful soore;
> And specially, for thy savacion
> Have I seyd many a precious orison . . .'

But he is readier to change the subject, and instead of enquiring after the invalid's health he talks of his own sermon ('There have I taught hem to be charitable'), for he is interested in Thomas only as a milch-cow. His interest in Thomas's wife is more personal. When she comes in,

> The frere ariseth up ful curteisly,
> And hire embraceth in his armes narwe,
> And kiste hire sweete, and chirketh as a sparwe;

and he replies to her greeting with honeyed flattery, calling himself her 'servant' (ambiguous and improper after his enthusiastic embrace), and protesting that she was the fairest woman in church that morning.

The wife, who later vanishes unobserved from the room and from the story, serves to reveal the friar's character here (like the cat earlier), but her principal use is to direct the conversation. The friar, pursuing his materialistic aim of getting money out of her husband, begs her to leave the two of them to their spiritual matters; and this allows her to complain of her husband's anger. Thus Chaucer prepares to connect the later developments of his story together. The wife's complaint brings in the friar's monologue against the deadly sin of anger. His monologue, in its turn, firstly increases the anger it is meant to allay, and directly produces Thomas's insult; and secondly shows up his own anger after the insult, thus leading on to his outraged arrival at the lord's house, and thence to the conclusion of the tale.

Before getting rid of Thomas's wife, Chaucer uses her to enlarge still further the character of the friar, whose reply to her question 'What wol ye dyne?' is a rich compound of affectation, epicurism, hypocrisy and flattery, and whose pretended vision of her dead baby borne to bliss is a masterpice of imaginative lying and fulsome sentiment ('With many a teere triklyng on my cheke'). This vision, and the whole friary's thanksgiving for it – in which, needless to say, the friar gives himself the leading part – starts him on a long and roundabout appeal for money. Beginning with the virtues which entitle friars to such visions and render their prayers acceptable to Christ –

'We lyve in poverte and in abstinence . . .

We han this worldes lust al in despit . . .

We fare as seith th'apostle; clooth and foode
Suffisen us, though they be nat ful goode . . .' –

he soon gets back to the theme of his morning sermon, the superiority of the friars to the monks who 'swymmen in possessioun'. By this time he has got Thomas to himself; and, his general remarks about friars' efficacious prayers suddenly reminding him that he is supposed to have been praying for Thomas's recovery, he as suddenly breaks into personal address:

'Therfore, right as an hauk up at a sours
Up springeth into th'eir, right so prayeres
Of charitable and chaste bisy freres
Maken hir sours to Goddes eres two.
Thomas! Thomas! so moote I ryde or go,
And by that lord that clepid is Seint Yve,
Nere thou oure brother, sholdestou nat thryve.
In our chapitre praye we day and nyght
To Crist, that he thee sende heele and myght
Thy body for to weelden hastily.'

The couplet is closed by Thomas's surly rejoinder, brutally direct:

'God woot,' quod he, 'no thyng therof feele I!
As help me Crist, as in a fewe yeres,
I have spent upon diverse manere freres
Ful many a pound; yet fare I never the bet' –

an unfortunate admission, for the friar seizes on it with a fierce quickness which foreshadows his own anger later, and proceeds to bully Thomas with a bombardment of rhetoric. Not only monks, but rival convents of friars, are his enemies. Besides revealing this new aspect of the friar's jealousy and greed, his argument hints that Chaucer has decided how he will finish the story:

'What is a ferthyng worth parted in twelve?
Lo, ech thyng that is oned in himselve
Is moore strong than whan it is toscatered.
Thomas, of me thou shalt nat been yflatered;
Thou woldest han oure labour al for noght.
The hye God, that al this world hath wroght,
Seith that the werkman worthy is his hyre.'

This anticipates Jankyn's

'Twelve spokes hath a cartwheel comunly'

and his

'The noble usage of freres yet is this,
The worthy men of hem shul first be served;
And certeinly he hath it weel disserved.'

Meanwhile, the friar reverts to Thomas's anger, for he is once more working round to shriving the sick man and then to soliciting a gift.

Chaucer manages the harangue with great success. He makes it tedious, pompous and shapeless; wearisome to Thomas but not to the reader. He tells the illustrative stories about angry kings with his usual pointed emphasis:

' "Ye shul be deed", quod he, "so moot I thryve!
That is to seyn, bothe oon, and two, and thre!" '

and with his usual vigour:

'And sodeynly he took his bowe in honde,
And up the streng he pulled to his ere,
And with an arwe he slow the child right there.'

Yet the inept use of these examples is not Chaucer's but

the friar's. When King Cambises shoots the child, the moral turns out to be

'Beth war, therfore, with lordes how ye pleye.
Syngeth *Placebo*, and "I shal, if I kan",
But if it be unto a povre man.
To a povre man men sholde his vices telle,
But nat to a lord, thogh he sholde go to helle.'

Likewise Thomas is warned against showing anger to his wife, not because anger is sinful, but because she is likely to repay it with interest:

'Be war, my sone, and herkne paciently,
That twenty thousand men han lost hir lyves
For stryvyng with hir lemmans and hir wyves.'

The dreadful prospect of twenty thousand examples is matched by the style of this complacent couplet, with its unspeakably monotonous second line:

'I koude of ire seye so muche sorwe,
My tale sholde laste til to-morwe.'

Thomas, has, in fact, preserved a remarkable outward patience. When the friar, unctuously calling him 'leeve brother', invites him to confess himself, he is content to reply that the parish priest has already heard his confession:

'I have be shryven this day at my curat.
I have hym toold hoolly al myn estat;
Nedeth namoore to speken of it', seith he,
'But if me list, of myn humylitee.'

This, besides being an implied rebuke to the friar for his earlier aspersions on priests ('Thise curatz been ful necligent and slowe . . .'), shows that Thomas is not an irreligious man, and thus gives greater point to his indignation against the friar – on whom, of course, the rebuke is quite lost. 'Yif me thanne of thy gold, to make oure cloystre' is his unabashed reply, and he pours out more praise of the indispensable friars, for whom he claims a pre-Christian antiquity:

> 'And that is nat of litel tyme', quod he,
> 'But syn Elye was, or Elise,
> Han freres been, that fynde I of record,
> In charitee, ythanked be oure Lord!
> Now, Thomas, help, for seinte charitee!'
> And doun anon he sette hym on his knee.
> This sike man wax wel ny wood for ire;
> He wolde that the frere had been on-fire,
> With his false dissymulacioun.

This is a delightful moment. Reaching the prepared climax of his appeal, the friar theatrically kneels, and a single grimace of fury seems to pass over the face of Thomas, making us ponder his calmly-expressed reply:

> 'Swich thyng as is in my possessioun',
> Quod he, 'that may I yeve yow, and noon oother. . .
>
> And in thyn hand thou shalt it have anon . . .
>
> A thyng that I have hyd in pryvetee.'

The dark ambiguity of Thomas's words, and his insistence on an oath that the gift shall be shared equally among all the friars, suggest to the friar that he will get something of great value:

> 'A!' thoghte this frere, 'that shal go with me!'

But to us who have just been given a glimpse of Thomas's rage, and can appreciate the covert sarcasm of his phrase 'my deere brother' (Thomas is now as cynical as the friar has always been), his offer is comically sinister. We therefore await the friar's discomfiture as eagerly as in *The Miller's Tale* we awaited that of Absolon first, and that of Nicholas later: for, like Absolon with the hot ploughshare, Thomas is ready:

> And whan this sike man felte this frere
> Aboute his tuwel grope there and heere,
> Amydde his hand he leet the frere a fart.
> Ther nys no capul, drawynge in a cart,
> That myghte have lete a fart of swich a soun.
> The frere up stirte as dooth a wood leoun.
> 'A! false cherl', quod he, 'for Goddes bones!
> This hastow for despit doon for the nones.
> Thou shalt abye this fart, if that I may!'
> His meynee, whiche that herden this affray,
> Cam lepynge in and chaced out the frere;
> And forth he gooth, with a ful angry cheere,
> And fette his felawe, ther as lay his stoor.
> He looked as it were a wilde boor;
> He grynte with his teeth, so was he wrooth.
> A sturdy paas doun to the court he gooth,
> Wher as ther woned a man of greet honour,
> To whom that he was alwey confessour.
> This worthy man was lord of that village.

The physical action, for which we have waited so long in this story, has come at last, and it is not disappointing. The full force of the insult to the friar, the weight of Thomas's accumulated contempt, is brought home by that reference to the cart-horse, while the raging lion and wild boar vividly suggest the friar's anger, his roar of fury and the gnashing of his teeth. The whole passage is dramatic. The friar, who has continued on his knees till now, violently leaps to his feet. The servants farcically come leaping *in* and chase *out* the friar in a single line.[1] The friar, on the wings of his rage, flies to the inn and drives down to the manor-house.

Thus is the relationship between the friar and his 'brother' Thomas brought to an end. Chaucer's immediate problem is to sustain our interest in what follows, and to connect the rest of the story with what has gone before.

He brilliantly avoids an anti-climax of his own by devising an anti-climax for the friar, whose calculated entrance falls completely flat:

> This frere cam as he were in a rage,
> Where as this lord sat etyng at his bord;
> Unnethes myghte the frere speke a word,
> Til atte laste he seyde, 'God yow see!'
> This lord gan looke, and seide, '*Benedicitee*!
> What, frere John, what maner world is this?
> I se wel that som thyng ther is amys;
> Ye looken as the wode were ful of thevys.
> Sit doun anon, and tel me what youre grief is,
> And it shal been amended, if I may.'

This gentleman, quietly attending to his own business at table, does not even see the melodramatic speechless

[1] This is the first and the last that we hear of these servants, who are wanted to speed the friar away and prevent his attacking Thomas. The contrast between his deliberate arrival and his unceremonious departure is very amusing. Incidentally, he never eats the dinner he so carefully orders, and so is still hungry when he arrives at the lord's house – where he finds the company at dinner.

arrival of the angry friar, and when he does notice him, his sobriety exposes the friar's extravagance.

> 'Sire', quod the lord, 'ye woot what is to doone.
> Distempre yow noght, ye be my confessour;
> Ye been the salt of the erthe and the savour.
> For Goddes love, youre pacience ye holde!
> Tel me youre grief'; and he anon hym tolde
> As ye han herd biforn, ye woot wel what.

The lord's remarks, without his intending it, are a rebuke to his confessor (and Thomas's) for not practising the self-control he preaches. His lady's sensible view of the case, 'A cherl hath doon a cherles dede', likewise throws into relief the friar's vow of revenge, which in its turn allows Chaucer to remind us of an important detail of what we have 'herd biforn' but may have forgotten amid the excitement:

> '. . . This false blasphemour, that charged me
> To parte that wol nat departed be,
> To every man yliche, with meschaunce!'

While this dialogue between the lady and the friar is going on, the lord muses on this subtle problem before him; and his treatment of it as a scholastic 'question', ideally capable of 'demonstracion', prepares us for Jankyn's solution of it by natural science, though at first sight it seems so insoluble as to be an invention of the devil ('I trowe the devel putte it in his mynde'; 'I holde hym certeyn a demonyak!'). However, when Jankyn's wit has solved the problem, Thomas's wit is credited with posing it.

Jankyn's solution is imaginative as well as clever. He

proposes a ceremonial occasion in this very hall, the twelve friars bearing their part in a ritual –

> 'Thanne shal they knele doun, by oon assent,
> And to every spokes ende, in this manere,
> Ful sadly leye his nose shal a frere' —

a ritual in which the bed-ridden Thomas, as donor, will perform his solemn part also, arriving with processional dignity:

> 'Thanne shal this cherl, with bely stif and toght
> As any tabour, hyder been ybroght.'

This vivid conception of the scene adds comic substance to the ingenious theory. It also relates all this latter part of the story to the satire on friars which is the main object of *The Summoner's Tale*. Jankyn arranges for Friar John to 'have the firste fruyt, as resoun is', because

> 'He hath to-day taughte us so muche good,
> With prechyng in the pulpit ther he stood,
> That I may vouche sauf, I sey for me,
> He hadde the firste smel of fartes thre.'

Thus the whole story is drawn together. Our minds are cast back to the friar's preaching with which the tale began, and to his harangue in the sick man's house. The problem of 'departynge of the fart on twelve' now falls into its proper, minor, place. It is not a necessary consequence of the scene at Thomas's, except in so far as Thomas has made the friar promise to divide the gift equally; and this condition is really imposed not by Thomas (who wants to insult the friar, not to set him a problem), but by Chaucer (who wants to keep the story going after its climax). The tale ends, therefore, with

Jankyn's speech repeating the insult of Thomas's action, and completing the friar's mortification.

The lord, the lady, and ech man, save the frere,
Seyde that Jankyn spak, in this matere,
As wel as Euclide dide or Ptholomee.
Touchynge the cherl, they seyde, subtiltee
And heigh wit made hym speken as he spak;
He nys no fool, ne no demonyak.
And Jankyn hath ywonne a newe gowne.
My tale is doon; we been almoost at towne.

There is no need for the Summoner to add his comments; he could do no more than tiresomely repeat the satirical points which the tale itself has already made against the friar.

VIII *The Merchant's Tale*

The Merchant's Tale of Januarie and May is by far the longest of Chaucer's comic tales, nearly twice as long as the second-longest, *The Miller's Tale*. Yet without the detailed satirical account of Januarie's motives for marrying May, the story would be less than a hundred lines longer than the Miller's. It could begin at the marriage, with the same kind of brief character-sketches as are given of the merchant and his wife in *The Shipman's Tale*, or of 'deynous Symkyn' and his family in *The Reeve's Tale*. Chaucer presumably heard the story in some such version. All its elements – as a mere story, that is, though Chaucer's treatment makes it a much richer thing – would be there: the marriage of age to youth, the old blind husband's deception by means of the pear-tree, the miraculous restoration of his sight, and the perhaps less miraculous provision of the wife's ready answer.

Nobody disputes the point that Chaucer's elaborate introduction is there in order to satirize foolish old Januarie and his marriage. What advantage this satirical introduction is to the tale, if any, and whether its tone is agreeable or unpleasant, are more debatable questions. Opinion has been divided between, at one extreme, those who think that the whole tale (its introduction in particular) reveals the bitter cynicism of its narrator the Merchant, whose prologue announces that he has been two months married to a shrew; and, at the other, those who think that the tale does not reveal its teller's personality at all, and that his unhappy marriage is an invention by Chaucer in order to find a teller for the tale.

Now certainly the tale is not told impersonally, like the greater part of the Miller's, for example. There is commentary, and plenty of it, as well as narration (though equally in *The Miller's Tale* the narrative is so handled as to imply an attitude). The opening implications about Januarie's decision to marry –

> Were it for hoolynesse or for dotage,
> I kan nat seye –

and the cool ironies about the necessary pleasures of marriage, are perfectly obvious, especially when the irony grows even cooler with the heated mock-indignation against detractors of marriage, such as Theofraste (God curse him!), followed by the dubious proof, by example of the creation of Eve,

> That wyf is mannes helpe and his confort,
> His paradys terrestre, and his disport.

This argument (incidentally, it is used with perfect seriousness in the *Tale of Melibeus*) amounts to an ironical version of the mock-denunciation in *The Nun's Priest's Tale*:

> Wommanes conseil broghte us first to wo,
> And made Adam fro Paradys to go.

The voice is familiar, and it is not that of the Merchant (which we have heard only in his matter-of-fact complaining prologue) but that of Chaucer. It is heard again, at a different pitch, inveighing against the cruel destiny that has made Januarie blind, or against the treachery of Damyan; these are the very tones in which Chauntecleer's evil destiny is lamented, or the treachery of Daun Russell the fox exposed. And both the satire and the moralizing are handled with gusto. The views about feminine helpfulness and the joys of marriage may be called cynical ones, but there is nothing which suggests a really jaundiced outlook on marriage or on life. Chaucer, the chameleon poet, has assumed the conventional satiric tone that his story calls for, and handles his traditional materials (he used Deschamps' *Miroir de Mariage* as an immediate source for his satire) like a virtuoso. He enjoys his own wooden-faced irony, and expects the reader to enjoy it too.

This spirit of satirical fun, harmonizing with the outbursts of extravagant rhetoric, colours the whole commentary. Of course Chaucer would not have affirmed upon oath these ironical remarks on marriage: he was too sensible to believe in this kind of generalization. But allowing for the conventional satire on women, his attitude to marriage (as to every subject) is absolutely wholesome. Januarie's marriage to May is not true marriage but a travesty of it. Damyan's adultery with May is not true courtly love but a travesty of that. We may grant that all three characters, and their doings, are unpleasant, but it does not follow that the author's attitude to life is unpleasant, or that reading the tale is an unpleasant experience as a whole. Like Ben Jonson's *Volpone*, and in much the same way, *The Merchant's Tale* is a wholesome serious treatment of an unpleasant subject. Also like *Volpone*, it is very funny; and the fun is usually at its height when the satire is at its most biting.

We may consider, as a foretaste of this quality before discussing Chaucer's handling of the whole story, the account of Januarie on his wedding day – and night. At the feast he gazes admiringly on his bride, vowing inwardly to embrace her 'harder than evere Parys dide Eleyne'; he speeds the guests before they are ready to depart, and when they have gone, and the bridal chamber is being blessed by the priest, the bridegroom applies himself with comic extravagance to aphrodisiacs

Swiche as the cursed monk, daun Constantyn,
Hath writen in his book *De Coitu*;
To eten hem alle he nas no thyng eschu.

At last the happy pair are alone,

And Januarie hath faste in armes take
His fresshe May, his paradys, his make.
He lulleth hire, he kisseth hire ful ofte;
With thikke brustles of his berd unsofte,
Lyk to the skyn of houndfyssh, sharp as brere –
For he was shave al newe in his manere –
He rubbeth hire aboute hir tendre face . . .

This is excellent comic poetry: its satiric force (felt in the brutal imagery, and in the contrast between this and the mock-romantic opening, in which 'paradys' is charged with the usual irony against Januarie) makes it not less but more comic. The soothing repeated rhythm of

He lulleth hire, he kisseth hire ful ofte

is hilariously contradicted by the rhyme-line

With thikke brustles of his berd unsofte;

and immediately we leap from the understatement of 'unsofte' to the wild hyperboles

Lyk to the skyn of houndfyssh, sharp as brere,

and to the paradoxical but convincing reason for this roughness, which takes us by delighted surprise:

> For he was shave al newe in his manere;

and then the whole is crowned by the reversion, in

> He rubbeth hire aboute hir tendre face,

to the soothing tones of the opening, while 'rubbeth' and 'tendre' insist comically on the satirical contrast between Januarie as he would like to appear and Januarie as he does appear.

This, then, is Chaucer's gusto and Chaucer's fun, and the whole of the tale exhibits its real teller (who is Chaucer, not the Merchant) in high spirits, fully enjoying his perfect control over the material he is using. He is in control both artistically and morally.

Here we must begin at the beginning, with the tale's long preamble about Januarie's character and his decision to marry, and the presumed benefits of marriage. The tale is essentially farcical, dealing with a wife's adultery in a pear-tree and her witty excuse; this farcical story is enriched by a satirical character-study of Januarie at full length, so to speak, with miniatures of Damyan and May, not to mention Januarie's friend and adviser (if one can call a sycophant an adviser) Placebo. The main target of satire is Januarie, which has encouraged some critics to suppose that by the image of Januarie's cause the Merchant sees – or fails to see – the portraiture of his own. But the Merchant has no character, only a situation.[1] There are better reasons for Chaucer's dwelling on

[1] A situation, moreover, which does not much resemble Januarie's. Chaucer tells us only that the Merchant's wife is a shrew, malicious, impatient and cruel. He tells us nothing of the Merchant's age, nor of his wife's, nor whether she was a maid or a widow when he married her.

Januarie and on marriage, and for his exhibiting character by dramatic means instead of by a brief summary. They are, first, that Januarie's character is amusing in itself, and offers Chaucer great opportunities of showing it off, thereby putting the reader into a good humour as well as putting him in possession of the necessary facts; and second, that Januarie's character needs to be developed in full satiric detail, so that his downfall is morally satisfying and at the same time richly comic. We must now see how the elaborate preamble works, and how Chaucer handles the rest of his narrative so as to be sure of the right kind of interest in the right place.

The tale opens with Januarie's character and situation. Chaucer's account of both is steeped in his hearty irony about marriage:

> Whilom ther was dwellynge in Lumbardye
> A worthy knyght, that born was of Pavye,
> In which he lyved in greet prosperitee;
> And sixty yeer a wyflees man was hee,
> And folwed ay his bodily delyt
> On wommen, ther as was his appetyt,
> As doon thise fooles that been seculeer.
> And whan that he was passed sixty yeer,
> Were it for hoolynesse or for dotage,
> I kan nat seye, but swich a greet corage
> Hadde this knyght to been a wedded man
> That day and nyght he dooth al that he kan
> T'espien where he myghte wedded be;
> Preyinge oure Lord to graunten him that he
> Mighte ones knowe of thilke blisful lyf
> That is bitwixe an housbonde and his wyf,
> And for to lyve under that hooly boond

With which that first God man and womman bond.
'Noon oother lyf', seyde he, 'is worth a bene;
For wedlok is so esy and so clene,
That in this world it is a paradys.'
Thus seyde this olde knyght, that was so wys.

We notice with surprise the 'worthy' knight's profligate history. Though his motives are left an open question by the author, we convict Januarie of hypocritical sanctimoniousness as well as of dotage; and when, after forty years or so as a libertine, he persuades himself that marriage is an earthly paradise, we see that he is in a fool's paradise, and that, since he desires the sweets of sin along with the safety of righteousness, it is fitting that he should thus enthusiastically run his head into the snare. Marriage is a 'bond': it is a contract, and also a bondage. This cynical view is a witty counterblast to Januarie's senseless optimism.

This point established (that marriage is bondage), and Januarie's character also established (he is a sophisticated but stupid old rake), Chaucer plays an ironical fantasy upon Januarie's wildly optimistic plans: old men in particular should marry, to beget heirs (the implication is that they should have done so before) and to enjoy the pleasant bondage which so differs from the wretched liberty of bachelors who sigh for love (like Damyan, one asks, after reading the story?); wives can do the impossible – both command and obey:

Ther nys no thyng in gree superlatyf,
As seith Senek, above an humble wyf.
Suffre thy wyves tonge, as Catoun bit;
She shal comande, and thou shalt suffren it,
And yet she wole obeye of curteisye.

The point of all this is to amuse the reader by putting him to a test which he can easily pass. Recognizing Chaucer's irony, we have passed this test, and are henceforth in league with him against Januarie. Just as we laugh at Chaucer's inconsistent justification of marriage in general, so we laugh at Januarie's inconsistent justification of his own motives for marriage.

Januarie has called his friends together not to discover their minds, but to speak his own. His recklessness has determined on marriage to a young girl, any young girl.[1] His vanity demands their approval. Consequently his long speech reveals his vice and folly, and at the same time gives us the satisfaction of picking holes in its illogicalities and shifts of viewpoint: thus, beginning with solemn sanctimoniousness –

> With face sad his tale he hath hem toold.
> He seyde, 'Freendes, I am hoor and oold,
> And almoost, God woot, on my pittes brynke;
> Upon my soule somwhat moste I thynke.
> I have my body folily despended;
> Blessed be God that it shal been amended! . . .'–

he ends by thanking God for a very different reason:

> 'For, God be thanked! I dar make avaunt,
> I feele my lymes stark and suffisaunt
> To do al that a man bilongeth to;
> I woot myselven best what I may do.
> Though I be hoor, I fare as dooth a tree
> That blosmeth er that fruyt ywoxen bee;

[1] Youth and beauty are all that he insists upon; and though later he indulges his fancy by comparing the 'maydens whiche that dwelten hym bisyde', taking such things as reputation into account, what chiefly 'passeth thurgh his herte nyght by nyght' is 'many fair shap and many a fair visage'.

And blosmy tree nys neither drye ne deed.
I feele me nowhere hoor but on myn heed;
Myn herte and alle my lymes been as grene
As laurer thurgh the yeer is for to sene.'

Januarie's perverse argument from imagery here (the double repetition of 'hoor' from the beginning of the speech marks how its course has changed, and the inapplicable simile of the 'blosmy tree' reminds us that he is really in his winter of life, not his spring) matches his travesty of logic throughout the speech, here for example:

'Wherfore I sey yow pleynly, in a clause,
I wol noon oold wyf han right for this cause.
For if so were I hadde swich myschaunce,
That I in hire ne koude han no pleasaunce,
Thanne sholde I lede my lyf in avoutrye,
And go streight to the devel, whan I dye.'

After such false conclusions as this, Placebo's praise of Januarie's reasoning and motives sounds like unconscious irony, and indeed repeats Chaucer's consciously ironical opening by praising Januarie's 'heigh corage'. For the present, however, we have had enough of irony, intentional or unintentional, and so Justinus's sober and outspoken reasoning comes as a relief, when he warns Januarie against a rash marriage:

'Senek, among his othere wordes wyse,
Seith that a man oghte hym right wel avyse
To whom he yeveth his lond or his catel.
And syn I oghte avyse me right wel
To whom I yeve my good awey fro me,
Wel muchel moore I oghte avysed be

To whom I yeve my body for alwey.
I warne yow wel, it is no childes pley
To take a wyf withouten avysement . . .'

Justinus is made human by his sorrowful experience in marriage ('But I woot best wher wryngeth me my sho'), and is made agreeable by his politeness. Januarie, in his rude reply, shows another side of his own disagreeable character:

'Wel', quod this Januarie, 'and hastow sayd?
Straw for thy Senek, and for thy proverbes!
I counte nat a panyer ful of herbes
Of scole-termes. Wyser men than thow,
As thou hast herd, assenteden right now
To my purpos. Placebo, what sey ye?'
'I seye it is a cursed man', quod he,
'That letteth matrimoigne, sikerly.'
And with that word they rysen sodeynly,
And been assented fully that he sholde
Be wedded whanne hym liste, and where he wolde.

This brings the scene to a vigorous and witty end. Januarie's use of the disrespectful 'thou' to Justinus contrasts sharply with his polite 'Placebo, what sey ye?'; and his speech is made more amusing by the fact that his 'wyser men', by whom he means Placebo, can in reality mean only Januarie himself, to whom Placebo is an obedient echo. Placebo's statement that to forbid matrimony is wicked reminds us that, on the contrary, Justinus is the only right-thinking man present. When the council is broken up, we are amused by the different ways in which Placebo, confirming Januarie's purpose, and Justinus, washing his hands of it,

been assented fully that he sholde
Be wedded whanne hym liste, and where he wolde.

Januarie, self-confirmed in his folly, is now shown acting on his absurd principles. He chooses a bride on insufficient grounds,

For love is blynd alday, and may nat see –

a useful foreshadowing of his physical blindness later, when Chaucer will make the point that Januarie has always been morally blind. Infatuated with her youth and beauty, he attributes to her all manner of virtues. He complacently reassembles his friends for no better purpose than to discuss the frivolous theological question of whether he will forfeit eternal bliss by having his heaven on earth in marriage; a question to which Justinus (who has the last word this time) replies with proper contempt and rich irony:

'Paraunter she may be youre purgatorie.'

An advantage of all this introductory matter is that when Chaucer comes to the events of the tale, he does not need to hold them up with explanations. His description of the marriage simultaneously cuts a long story short and throws out broad hints which his ironic introduction has made us ready to take: blessing the ill-assorted couple, the priest 'made al siker ynogh with hoolynesse', but we suspect that all will not be sure and safe. The feast is described in all its splendour. Chaucer enjoys the bustling activity, for which we also have an appetite after the amusing but essentially static preliminaries, and of course he never forgets that the feast is really a celebration of the bridegroom's lust and folly:

Bacus the wyn hem shynketh al aboute,
And Venus laugheth upon every wight,
For Januarie was bicome hir knyght,
And wolde both assayen his corage
In libertee, and eek in mariage;
And with hire fyrbrond in hire hand aboute
Daunceth biforn the bryde and al the route.
And certeinly, I dar right wel seyn this,
Ymeneus, that god of weddyng is,
Saugh nevere his lyf so myrie a wedded man.

Venus, as we learn, has burned Damyan with her firebrand; and though, in the lines immediately following, Januarie plans to act the part of Paris in his bed that night, the sudden unexpected appearance of Damyan in the story suggests that Menelaus is the husband's more probable rôle. Damyan, like a courtly lover, retires to his sorrowful bed, Chaucer dropping an ambiguous hint that May will pity him before long, and thus neutralizing the pathos of his situation, and of hers. Chaucer's warning apostrophe to Januarie, 'dronken in plesaunce', and his scandalized exclamation

God graunte thee thyn hoomly fo t'espye!

reveal another purpose of the long introduction: we hope that Januarie will *not* discover Damyan's intentions, and that he will be proved the fool he is. We hope this especially when Januarie retires to his bridal bed, an absurd yet disgusting travesty of a lover, gloating over what amounts to his rape of May.

The story resumes four days later with May's reappearance in the hall at meals. She has kept her room,

For every labour somtyme moot han reste,

and while she languishes from too much of Januarie's love, Damyan languishes from too little of hers. His absence is noted by Januarie, who, with fine dramatic irony, urges May to visit the invalid and 'dooth hym disport'. This prepares for the more farcical dramatic irony of the garden scene, where Januarie is literally a go-between in the encounter of Damyan and May.

The romantic element in their first encounter is deliberately reduced by Damyan's self-interest in preserving secrecy (his life, not the lady's reputation, is the important respect), and by May's prudence in getting rid of the love-letter in the privy. Chaucer, who is no cynic, is far from applauding their conduct – in many a Restoration comedy of intrigue, the Damyan-figure would be the hero – but he explains it by returning May directly to the bed of Januarie, who, by reason of his old age and utter selfishness, has no right to her either; and who, though she may be his paradise, is certainly her hell. Therefore, at the first occasion, the all-too-pitying May declares her love to Damyan, who recovers from his malady with farcical speed ('Up riseth Damyan the nexte morwe' – we see him bounce out of bed). All this is what Januarie's faults have made us hope, though the fact that we expected nothing better of the lovers makes us properly contemptuous of them.

Here is the story's point of balance. With a secret understanding reached between May and Damyan, and Januarie as besotted in joy as ever, events are ready to develop. But instead of directly and obviously developing them, Chaucer very skilfully sets to work in a roundabout manner, discussing felicity in general, Januarie's felicity in particular, and such material tokens of this as his housing and his array. One such token is a private garden walled with stone.

> So faire a gardyn woot I nowher noon.
> For, out of doute, I verraily suppose
> That he that wroot the Romance of the Rose
> Ne koude of it the beautee wel devyse;
> Ne Priapus ne myghte nat suffyse,
> Though he be god of gardyns, for to telle
> The beautee of the gardyn and the welle,
> That stood under a laurer alwey grene.
> Ful ofte tyme he Pluto and his queene
> Proserpina, and al hire fayerye,
> Disporten hem and maken melodye
> Aboute that welle, and daunced, as men tolde.

This indirect approach sets the now practised reader to work again. The passage opens with Januarie's general happiness in order to prepare us for his misfortune in becoming blind; but Chaucer must not state this misfortune so suddenly that we recognize it for what it is, a necessity of the plot. Yet we can guess that this garden, on which Chaucer is spending some time, is not just an illustration of Januarie's happiness, but will play some important part; and we guess its connexion with love before we are told of the use Januarie makes of it. The *Romance of the Rose* suggests the idealized world of the love-allegories; but Priapus, who is the god of something else besides gardens, adds coarse practice to this refined theory. He also, as classical deity (like Bacchus, Venus and Hymen at the wedding), harmonizes with Pluto and Proserpine, whose fairy powers will be taxed later, and whose mention now makes us accept their intervention then. Perhaps, too, the phallic god is connected satirically with the evergreen laurel, and with Januarie's memorable boast that his heart and all his limbs were as fresh and green as that laurel.

To Januarie Chaucer now turns:

> This noble knyght, this Januarie the olde,
> Swich deyntee hath in it to walke and pleye,
> That he wol no wight suffren bere the keye
> Save he hymself; for of the smale wyket
> He baar alwey of silver a clyket,
> With which, whan that hym leste, he it unshette.
> And whan he wolde paye his wyf hir dette
> In somer seson, thider wolde he go,
> And May his wyf, and no wight but they two;
> And thynges whiche that were nat doon abedde,
> He in the gardyn parfourned hem and spedde.

The garden, devoted to love, is his special preserve, and his selfish enjoyment of the garden is linked with his uxorious selfishness (which his blindness will increase into jealousy) by the implied sexual imagery of the small wicket gate and the private key, an implication reinforced by the immediately following lines about paying his wife her debt. In thus choosing to enjoy his wife *al fresco*, Januarie shows himself once more a connoisseur of licentious variety (the narrator is emphatically reticent about his behaviour both in bed and in the garden); and furthermore, this use of the garden helps to soften our incredulity when we arrive at the doings in the pear-tree. That the story is set in sunny Italy is relevant to both these aspects of it.

Thus Chaucer naturally (but very skilfully) arrives at Januarie's blindness, at the same time preparing for the rest of the plot and setting its scene. Now he can exclaim against fortune's cruelty towards Januarie, and rely on us to remember that Januarie selfishly abused his good fortune, and to feel that he deserves affliction for a change.[1] Further, the old man's blindness inflames his jealousy; and the jealousy both frustrates his wife's desire to cuckold him, and also maintains our hostility towards him (which his blindness might reduce, if he did not so obviously keep all his vices), so that we feel he is justly served when Damyan enjoys the jealously-secured May in the jealously-secured garden.

As with Alison and Nicholas in *The Miller's Tale*, Chaucer does not tell us all the lovers' plan, and he thus keeps us in suspense –

> Som wonder by this clyket shal bityde,
> Which ye shul heeren, if ye wole abyde –

and the pleasant expectation that Januarie will somehow be fooled, just as surely as was John the carpenter, 'for al his kepyng and his jalousye'. At the same time, the comment that love always finds out a way –

> O noble Ovyde, ful sooth seystou, God woot,
> What sleighte is it, thogh it be long and hoot,
> That Love nyl fynde it out in som manere?
> By Piramus and Tesbee may men leere . . . –

reminds us that the love of Damyan and May, though it is more natural than Januarie's senile lustfulness, is

[1] With this intent, Chaucer handles the passage of time very flexibly. Damyan's passion begins at the very moment of Januarie's marriage, and the progress of his affair with May is a rapid one; yet Januarie's blindness, though a 'sodeyn hap' when it comes, does not seem to come very soon after his marriage, for he uses his garden 'in somer seson' (implying that in winter he uses his bedroom), and enjoys 'many a murye day'. Thus, in spite of the zodiacal references which confine the action to a few months, Januarie's happiness seems to extend over at least a year.

simply physical desire, even if it is dressed up in romantic trappings, and is thus hardly comparable with that of Pyramus and Thisbe.

'But now to purpos' – and the story moves to its climax. With May's encouragement, Januarie invites her into the garden with his unbecoming paraphrase of the Song of Solomon, while she in turn invites Damyan with equally eloquent gesture. Januarie's elaborate precautions with the gate, and his confidence that he and May are alone, fix the farcical spirit of everything that follows; while Damyan's sudden entry into the 'fresshe' garden, 'fresshe' being the constant epithet for May, foreshadows his seduction of her (when 'in he throng' with equal suddenness):

> This Damyan thanne hath opened the wyket,
> And in he stirte, and that in swich manere
> That no wight myghte it se neither yheere,
> And stille he sit under a bussh anon.
> This Januarie, as blynd as is a stoon,
> With Mayus in his hand, and no wight mo,
> Into his fresshe gardyn is ago,
> And clapte to the wyket sodeynly.
> 'Now wyf', quod he, 'heere nys but thou and I . . .'

But Chaucer is concerned with more than farcical plot here: he is concerned with moral character; and that the two harmonize instead of conflicting is the mark of his genius. Januarie's next words are an appeal to May to be always true to him. This is Chaucer's boldest stroke, for he cannot risk engaging pity for Januarie (which would make the story disagreeable by impeding its moral satire), yet he wants to stress the dramatic irony and along with this the perfidy of May (because the *dénoue-*

ment will turn upon her ready answer). Thus Januarie's appeal is coloured by selfishness, and May's reply, a tactical triumph with its tearful general countercharge against husbandly suspicion, shows her typical feminine subtlety[1]:

'Why speke ye thus? but men been evere untrewe,
And wommen have repreve of yow ay newe . . .'

And at the very same moment she is pointing up the pear-tree, which Damyan promptly climbs.

The farcical scene is set. And now comes a second bold stroke of Chaucer's, for he drops the curtain, leaving Damyan up the tree and the married pair walking in the garden, while he himself, at conscious length, talks about the weather ('Bright was the day, and blew the firmament . . .'). He thus makes a comic virtue out of the fact that the story must stand still while Pluto and Proserpine are brought in.

May's countercharge in reply to Januarie's suspicious speech has set the tone of Pluto's dialogue with his queen. Their subject, implied in the traditional satire of the whole tale, is woman's inhumanity to man:

'My wyf', quod he, 'ther may no wight seye nay;
Th'experience so preveth every day
The tresons whiche that wommen doon to man.'

He talks like the clerk Jankyn, and Proserpine replies like the Wife of Bath. The upshot is that they resolve to be not only auditors but actors too in the mortals' drama before their eyes. Pluto will restore Januarie's sight,

1 'For al swich wit is yeven us in oure byrthe;
Deceite, wepyng, spynnyng God hath yive
To wommen kyndely, whil that they may lyve.'
The Wife of Bath's Prologue, 400-402.

Proserpine provide May's excuse.[1] The approaching *dénouement* thus takes on a new interest: we await not only the solution to a practical problem, as in *The Miller's Tale* (how will adultery be contrived?), but also the solution to a theoretical one, as in *The Summoner's Tale* (how will the seemingly impossible – in this case, May's innocence – be demonstrated?).

This double resolution now proceeds. The practical problem is solved at once by May's pretended pregnancy:

> This fresshe May, that is so bright and sheene,
> Gan for to syke, and seyde, 'Allas, my syde!
> Now sire,' quod she, 'for aughte that may bityde,
> I moste han of the peres that I see,
> Or I moot dye, so soore longeth me
> To eten of the smale peres grene.
> Help, for hir love that is of hevene queene!
> I telle yow wel, a womman in my plit
> May han to fruyt so greet an appetit
> That she may dyen, but she of it have.'
> 'Allas!' quod he, 'that I ne had heer a knave
> That koude clymbe! Allas, allas', quod he,
> 'That I am blynd!' 'Ye, sire, no fors', quod she;
> 'But wolde ye vouche sauf, for Goddes sake,
> The pyrie inwith youre armes for to take,
> For wel I woot that ye mystruste me,
> Thanne sholde I clymbe wel ynogh', quod she,
> 'So I my foot myghte sette upon youre bak.'

[1] This is a great improvement on those analogues in which St Peter asks God to restore the husband's sight, and God predicts that the wife will show her woman's wit by her ready answer. Proserpine, moreover, having been herself an unwilling bride – 'Which that he ravysshed out of Ethna, / Whil that she gadered floures in the mede' – has a second reason for taking May's part.

The ultimate farcical ironies are reached when Januarie regrets the absence of a servant who could climb the tree, and himself helps his wife to the arms of 'his owene man' up there. As farce this is perfect, but since the tale is a moral satire also, May's ready excuse and her gulling of Januarie is the more weighty climax of the two, as it should be. And here appears a further usefulness of Januarie's appeal to May's loyalty, and her reply. For although she owes to Proserpine the substance of her answer, its protesting and injured tone belongs wholly to herself: 'This thank have I for I have maad yow see.' Once more, Chaucer shows his interest in moral character. May has the very promising makings of a shrew, and offers to be Januarie's purgatory in every way. She bullies him into condoning, not only her recent action, but her future ones;

'Til that youre sighte ysatled be a while,
Ther may ful many a sighte yow bigile.'

The end of the story is unusual among Chaucer's comic tales in that it looks beyond the action that we see, into the future. The credulous Januarie, self-satisfied as ever, and glorying now in his prospects of fatherhood, complacently makes much of May in the rhythms and rhymes of the wedding-night couplets:

He kisseth hire, and clippeth hire ful ofte,
And on hire wombe he stroketh hire ful softe,
And to his paleys hoom he hath hire lad.
Now, goode men, I pray yow to be glad.
Thus endeth heere my tale of Januarie;
God blesse us, and his mooder Seinte Marie!

Of course, after Damyan's services, the pregnancy of

May has become a distinct possibility. Once again, this is Chaucer's fun, a light-hearted innuendo and not a disagreeable one; and his valediction (or the Merchant's if we will, for as usual the narrator is in at the finish),[1] is to be taken literally:

> Now, goode men, I pray yow to be glad.

One of Thomas Hardy's characters, gratefully accepting a mug of cider which is dirt-encrusted through standing among the warm ashes on the hearth, engagingly observes: 'I never fuss about dirt in its pure state, and when I know what sort it is.' *The Merchant's Tale* is dirty enough, like some of the other comic ones, in its way; but Chaucer's sureness of touch, as an artist and as a man, makes the dirt a pure kind of dirt, and the story one at which we can be glad.

[1] He has appeared earlier (or Chaucer has), refusing to describe Januarie's love-making, 'lest that precious folk be with me wrooth'; and apologizing when May climbs the tree to Damyan –

> Ladyes, I prey yow that ye be nat wrooth;
> I kan nat glose, I am a rude man –

and when Januarie, looking aloft with his restored sight,

> saugh that Damyan his wyf had dressed
> In swich manere it may nat been expressed,
> But if I wolde speke uncurteisly.

Chaucer uses this affected delicacy of style in order to bring out the real indelicacy of the action, much as he has used his apology for *The Miller's Tale* to bring out the robust coarseness of its climax.

Index